YOUR
EMOTIONAL
HEALTH
AND
WELL-BEING

THE NO NONSENSE LIBRARY

NO NONSENSE HEALTH GUIDES

Women's Health and Fitness
A Diet for Lifetime Health
A Guide to Exercise and Fitness Equipment
How to Tone and Trim Your Trouble Spots
Stretch for Health
Unstress Your Life
Calories, Carbohydrates and Sodium
Permanent Weight Loss
All about Vitamins and Minerals
Reducing Cholesterol

NO NONSENSE FINANCIAL GUIDES

NO NONSENSE REAL ESTATE GUIDES

NO NONSENSE LEGAL GUIDES

NO NONSENSE CAREER GUIDES

NO NONSENSE SUCCESS GUIDES

NO NONSENSE COOKING GUIDES

NO NONSENSE WINE GUIDES

NO NONSENSE PARENTING GUIDES

NO NONSENSE STUDENT GUIDES

YOUR EMOTIONAL HEALTH AND WELL-BEING

How to Cope with Stress and Feel Better Fast

By the Editors of
PREVENTION® Magazine

Longmeadow Press

Notice

This book is intended as a reference volume only, not as a medical manual or guide to self-treatment. It is not intended as a substitute for the medical advice of physicians. The reader should regularly consult a physician in general, and particularly for any symptoms. If you suspect that you have a medical problem, we urge you to seek competent medical help. Keep in mind that exercise and nutritional needs vary from person to person, depending on age, sex, health status and individual variations. The information here is intended to help you make informed decisions about your health, not as a substitute for any treatment that may have been prescribed by your doctor.

Your Emotional Health and Well-Being

Published January 1989 by Longmeadow Press, 201 High Ridge Road, Stamford, CT 06904. No part of this book may be reproduced or used in any form or by any means, electronic or mechanical, including photocopying, recording, or by any information storage and retrieval system, without permission in writing from the publisher.

Library of Congress Cataloging-in-Publication Data

Your emotional health and well-being.

    (No nonsense health guide)
      1. Stress management.   2. Mental health.
I. Prevention (Emmaus, Pa.)   II. Series: No nonsense health guide.
RA785.Y68   1989   158′.1   88-37739
ISBN 0-681-40717-4 paperback

Compiled and edited by Marcia Holman and Jane Sherman

Book design by Acey Lee
Cover illustration by Jean Gardner

Photographs by Angelo M. Caggiano pp. 15, 35; Donna M. Hornberger p. 61; Mitchell T. Mandel pp. 70, 89; Alison Miksch p. 57; Rodale Press Photography Department pp. 4, 19, 42, 77.

No Nonsense Health Guide is a trademark controlled by Longmeadow Press.

2 4 6 8 10 9 7 5 3 1   paperback

Contents

A Balanced "Diet" for the Mind

Thoughts and emotions are the nutrients of the mind.

Just as we need a certain balance of vitamins, protein and other nutrients to help our bodies reach maximum energy levels, each of us needs a specific balance of mental "nutrients" for a happy, tranquil and creative mind.

Not so long ago, the popular belief was that emotional health was something you either had or didn't have. Sigmund Freud, perhaps the most well known of the early psychologists, believed that character and personality were formed in very early childhood, influenced by experiences that were then repressed and became part of the "unconscious." In later life, any attempt to change would meet with failure because we were helpless to fight those urges and impulses buried within us. Today, however, when mental health is evaluated by such diverse measures as the ability to give and accept love, to change your mind or alter your habits, to take reasonable chances or to bounce back from stress, there is more hope for change.

The new holistic psychology says that it is within our power to alter the way we feel. We act a certain way, even feel a certain way, not because of our unconscious programming but because we have *learned* this behavior. And if we have learned one way of thinking, we can learn another. What's more, says the new psychology, it's our *responsibility* to create the good, positive feelings that make life worth living.

The new mind mentors also tell us—and prove it through countless studies—that our mental attitude is a powerful influence on our physical health. Thus, our power to control and reshape our attitudes and emotions serves a double purpose: happiness *and* health.

In *Your Emotional Health and Well-Being,* you'll find information on understanding your moods and changing them for the better, increasing self-esteem, dealing with sexual problems, enhancing your learning ability, using pets and plants to defuse stress, and much more. In short, you'll learn how to apply some of the new knowledge of emotional health to help yourself to a more positive outlook and a healthier, more satisfying life.

C H A P T E R

O N E

The Potent Power of the Imagination

Long before the real race is run, world-class track star James Robinson is running it in his mind, rehearsing every second of the half-mile as surely as he practiced each day on the track. The image is so clear he can hear his heartbeat, feel the cinders crunching under his shoes and see himself surge ahead near the end to lean through the tape.

When all the athletes in a race are in virtually the same tip-top shape, it's presence of mind that makes the difference.

Lester L., a Florida businessman, was running a different race— for his life. A tumor had invaded his throat. It was going to have to come out, and with it possibly his vocal cords.

A week before the operation, Lester started an imaginary attack on his tumor. His white blood cells became busy miners with pickaxes, hacking away at the mass. Once fearful of surgery, Lester now imagined that it would go well. He saw himself controlling his bleeding during surgery and recovering quickly. When the doctor did operate, the tumor was half its expected size. Lester awakened as he left the operating room, and he was on the phone two hours later. He left the hospital in two days. Just a coincidence? Lester doesn't think so.

Sarah M., a Boston journalist, had embarked on a new career as a free-lance writer, something she'd always wanted to do. But she was having trouble writing. She couldn't take herself seriously. She was afraid she'd fail and indeed seemed to be setting herself up for just that.

Instead, she learned to imagine her new self at parties, talking with confidence and self-respect about her career change. She also gained a strong new image of sitting down and writing for a full day without distractions. Pie-in-the-sky fantasies? Not for Sarah. She's already started doing the same things in real life, and her writing career has taken off.

So what's going on here? Are we to believe that if we think about something hard enough and long enough and in enough detail, it will become real?

Yes, to a large extent. We *can* maximize our potential, both in performance and in health, and within the realm of possibility. And there's good evidence to show that our potential goes far beyond what we think of as normal, everyday functioning.

Tricking the Subconscious

One widely held theory for imagery's powerful effect is that it fools the subconscious mind. The subconscious, it seems, cannot always tell the difference between an actual experience and a vivid image. And that's one reason researchers think imagery can so easily produce physical responses. Image a near miss in your car and your blood pressure, pulse rate and adrenaline levels soar. See yourself on a sunny beach and watch them drop.

It was this sort of observation that convinced Jeanne Achterberg, Ph.D., a leading researcher and author in the field, that there was a definite link between the imagination and the body's healing process.

Dr. Achterberg states that in the medical literature on people who recovered despite a diagnosis of terminal cancer, the only thing in common was a change of attitude. "Something happened to cause them to begin to have a different image of themselves—not of a dying person but of a well person," she says. In her clinical practice, Dr. Achterberg observes that "someone would come in with total liver failure, yellow as a pumpkin, and be up and walking around in two weeks. Another person would have a simple diagnosis of a small breast tumor and soon be dead.

"Now this goes beyond physiology. You cannot die from a small breast tumor. It doesn't impinge on any vital organs. But you *can* die from giving up. You can die from the workings of the imagination. And from it you can also gain life."

The Imagery of Cancer

How? By "seeing" yourself as a healthy, whole person despite what the doctors say. Doing so actually beefs up the immune system, cuts down on stress and may give you a new lease on life, Dr. Achterberg says. "I am not saying this is for everyone, or that anyone can do it," she emphasizes. "It takes 100 percent commitment, and sometimes the body is just too worn out and tired for this sort of thing." And one of the prerequisites seems to be that you have to really believe that it will work for you.

Dr. Achterberg found that terminal cancer patients who went into remission or experienced shrinkage of their tumor not only had an incredible will to live, they also imagined their cancer, their immune system and their treatment in a certain, positive way.

One man, for instance, saw his cancer as small, easily squashed creatures being lanced by white knights on horses—his own white blood cells. "Having images of goodness and purity of the immune system was important," she says. So was being able to see a treatment as effective and safe. One woman imaged her radiation as the healing rays of the sun; another saw her chemotherapy as a powerful substance that exploded her cancer cells the instant it touched them.

Imagery can be a basis for diagnosis, Dr. Achterberg believes. "It could be that those who saw white knights were simply getting in touch with the intuitive sense that tells us what's going on in the body. And that those whose cancers were imagined as ants or crabs—clinging, pinching images that meant a poor prognosis for recovery—somehow sensed that they weren't going to get well."

The question now is whether changing these images into a more positive form can help to fight the disease. Preliminary research seems to indicate that it can, Dr. Achterberg says, although she emphasizes that very few people have actually done so. "Only recently have we begun to get some work showing that if the images are changed, you actually get changes in the healing mechanism of the body itself."

In one study, conducted by Howard Hall, Psy.D., Ph.D., of Pennsylvania State University, certain people (those who are younger or more susceptible to hypnosis) who twice each day for a week imagined their germ-killing white blood cells as sharks showed a significant increase in number of white blood cells. Several repeats of this and similar tests have shown the same results, Dr. Achterberg says.

And researchers at Michigan State University demonstrated that

The imagination is a powerful force, with the potential to change our lives for the better. Taking a break to picture yourself in a peaceful setting like this, for instance, may soothe anxiety, help you think more clearly and allow you to be more efficient at whatever task you face.

people could change the number and function of a specific white blood cell, called a neutrophil, by first seeing actual pictures of the blood cell and then, under induced relaxation, imaging the process by which the blood cells act. Bordering on science fiction? Perhaps. But Dr. Achterberg envisions a day when people will help themselves to heal with images of knitting bone tissue, dilated arteries and an army of white blood cells coming to their defense.

Walking Tightropes and Chasing Butterflies

California psychologist James Meade, Jr., Ph.D., uses imagery to help brain-injured adults walk and talk again. A man who was having trouble with balance learned to see himself as a tightrope walker, an image that forced his brain to make subtle balance corrections. He also learned to no longer fear falling. If he imagined himself slipping off the rope, he'd then see himself catching the rope, pulling himself up and continuing along.

Another man, depressed and with many coordination problems, learned how to move his arms and walk again with the aid of a most pleasant scene. From his hospital bed, he would imagine himself in a field of wildflowers, catching beautiful butterflies in a net, then examining them and releasing them to fly again.

Drunk Self/Sober Self

Drug addicts and alcoholics who successfully kick the habit share a common image, says Lawrence Horberg, Ph.D., a Chicago psychologist specializing in drug addiction. "They can bring back quite strongly a picture of themselves doing something that can be humiliating and degrading or resulting in personal loss. This negative image can be a powerful source of motivation in the lifelong struggle to remain drug free." One cocaine addict, for instance, could see himself combing his carpet for a trace of the spilled powder.

Typically, addicts *can't* remember such scenes. Drugs and alcohol and ordinary psychological defenses block their awareness. The details are stored in the brain, though, and can be retrieved in the form of imagery. Dr. Horberg provides a supportive environment and encourages the patient to listen to family, friends and employers recount scenes of addiction or intoxication. Then he uses a similar technique to help the addict create a healthy, happy image of his new, sober self.

Image Your Best Self

You don't have to be an addict to benefit from developing a new self-image. Timothy Hodgens, Ph.D., a Westborough, Massachusetts, psychologist, uses imagery in perhaps its largest sense—to help people gain a sense of themselves, their goals and their place in life.

"Many people who go through therapy and discover some of their problems get scared when they start trying to change," Dr. Hodgens says. "They don't want to continue as they are, but they have no idea who it is they eventually want to be and how they are going to get there."

To help them tackle this problem, Dr. Hodgens asks them to image themselves during a time when they felt things were going well, when everything seemed to come together. For him, that time was when he had just finished giving a speech at a conference.

The next step is to start talking with your ideal self and to listen to what it has to say to you. "Everyone has to ask their own, very personal questions, but it's in this dialogue that new insights are uncovered."

The final step, a lifelong process, really is to project yourself into your image of your ideal self. "It becomes a transformation," Dr. Hodgens says. "Over a period of time you start to lose your old self in the process. You project yourself into that image, right now, and then begin to see yourself feeling, acting, behaving in that way and that context.

"There has to be a very serious intent of moving toward this best possible self. It's not easy, but it's possible."

New Help for Sexual Problems

Some deal with it by slipping into the library for self-help manuals. Braver souls schedule a doctor's appointment "for a . . . uh, um . . . problem." Many merely muffle sad sighs into the pillow, night after night.

As one man put it, "Sexual problems have got to be *the* hardest thing in the world to talk about with anyone."

Sexual dysfunction is at least becoming less difficult to treat, if not discuss. The fields of sexual medicine and psychosexual therapy are yielding answers to the distressing but not uncommon question, "Why can't I make love?"

When the Body Won't

Nearly ten million American men share the problem of impotence, a condition sort of like a started car with four flat tires that can't go anywhere. It's a matter of faulty mechanics: Impotent men may *desire* sex, but their bodies are unable to achieve and maintain erections capable of vaginal penetration.

7

Almost every man goes through some *brief* period of impotence at least once in his life. This is probably normal and could just be the result of not enough sleep, worry about a career or the mortgage, or other stress.

"A few weeks of this temporary impotence is nothing to worry about," says Jack Jaffe, M.D., medical director of the Potency Recovery Center in Los Angeles (Panorama City), California. "When months go by, though, some concern may be in order and a cause should be sought."

The cause might be psychogenic, calling for counseling to explore why the mind has put up a roadblock to sex. Fear of impregnating a woman or a trigger event such as an extramarital affair are only two of the many explanations physicians discover. "Doctor, I was fine until about two weeks ago . . . " is one clue that the impotence is psychologically rooted.

But in roughly 30 to 50 percent of all impotency cases, the trouble is organic, or physical, in nature. "A tip-off to organic impotency is if the patient says, 'I can't figure it out—it just sort of eased up on me and got gradually worse,'" explains Michael Pfeifer, M.D., an endocrinologist and associate professor of medicine at the University of Louisville School of Medicine.

Diabetes, atherosclerosis, high blood pressure and other medical conditions are frequently to blame. (As many as half of all diabetic men become impotent.) In addition to the illnesses themselves, the medications used to treat them often invite impotence.

To first determine if the impotence is of a psychogenic or organic nature, doctors study penis activity during REM sleep, the stage where dreams and (usually) multiple erections take place.

"Blood flow increases in REM sleep and swells the penis," Dr. Pfeifer says. (The equivalent of this in women is a vaginal flush.) "But if a medical problem interferes with blood flow, the penis will stay flaccid. The oldest method to monitor REM activity used a strip of postage stamps wrapped around the shaft. In the morning, if the perforations were broken, we could assume an erection had taken place and the man was physically capable of having intercourse. Therefore we told him, 'You're normal; the problem is with your mind or your desire.' But what we really were seeing was evidence of tumescence, or soft swelling, and not rigidity, the full hardness needed to make love."

Two monitoring improvements were developed that could tell

where on the penis—the base, shaft or tip—response was lacking. But with a new robotic-type device, doctors can assess rigidity for the first time. "This is exciting—now we can truly differentiate between psychogenic and organic trouble," says Dr. Pfeifer. The device is called a rigiscan, and it can assess tumescence and rigidity at the base and tip during sleep. It consists of two bands around the penis, with wires that connect to a computer chip attached to the leg. The memory chip can then be played back on a computer in the morning for a truer-than-ever picture of erectile ability.

If two to five nights of REM testing indicate a physical problem, further medical screening can look for hormonal trouble, which shows up in 2 to 4 percent of impotency cases and can usually be successfully treated by an endocrinologist; vascular impairment, which keeps enough blood from getting to the penis in 10 to 30 percent of impotent men and can respond to new, intricate vein and artery surgery; or nerve problems, determined mainly by a diagnosis of exclusion.

Some Helpful Technology

When the bottom line is impotence that can't be cured by eliminating the physical condition, technology offers four possible ways to produce erections strong enough for making love. They're listed here from least to most recommended by doctors.

Vasodilators. These are oral medications (yohimbine and nitroglycerin) used with mild success to dilate blood vessels. "This approach is still experimental, and there are better options," Dr. Jaffe notes.

Injections. The drugs papaverine and phentolamine combine in this new concept of self-administered penile shots. Increased blood flow produces the fullest, most natural-looking erection of any artificial aid and will last 30 to 120 minutes.

Suction devices. Resembling either condoms or cylinders, the two new suction methods create a vacuum to make an erection that will last about a half hour. "This might be a good method if you don't want one of the other approaches and can't undergo surgery for an implant," says Dr. Pfeifer, "but there are minuses: The penis gets stiff but not really hard. Sperm are blocked by the rubber band used to keep blood in the penis, and fathering children can't happen. [It's not to be used as a birth control method, though.] And there's extreme danger to the organ if the man falls asleep and doesn't take off the rubber band."

Prostheses.   Penile implants get the highest marks from physicians and from most of the 350,000 men in America who have them. Seventeen studies by 25 urologists indicate over 90 percent of the men and women whose sex lives depend upon a prosthesis accept it and are emotionally satisfied with the results.

Although the idea of penile implants is not new (men have been getting them for more than 20 years), there have been tremendous improvements in design and function.

In Dr. Pfeifer's opinion, "An implant carries less risk than other impotence treatments, is more romantic because it allows spontaneity, lets the man father children and gives a better-quality sex life."

There are several styles of implants available. One is the semirigid type. During simple, inexpensive surgery, two flexible rods are implanted in the penis that allow a man to bend it up for intercourse and down close to the body when not in use. "There are no parts to break down with this version," says Dr. Jaffe, "but the man is still somewhat stiff and elongated when not making love."

Another implant is inflatable. Balloon-shaped implant material makes a penis with this aid look more natural when erect and truly flaccid afterward. The man pumps an implanted reservoir to harden (it takes effort to inflate) and can achieve large, full-girth erections. "This method seems to give the highest satisfaction to couples," notes Dr. Pfeifer. The drawbacks: Many parts are involved and in some cases will need repair in one to five years. Also, it requires longer, more invasive surgery and is more expensive.

The self-contained type of implant also uses the pump concept, but it is combined with rods. It has fewer parts than the inflatable and is less complicated to install. The penis with a self-contained implant will look only semiflaccid when not erect, "a potential problem for men who shower in a gym after a workout or similar social situation," Dr. Pfeifer says.

A fourth prosthesis will be available soon; it consists of a ball, socket and rod-type design and "works like clicking a ballpoint pen to become erect and then flaccid," explains Dr. Pfeifer. The appearance of the penis will be neither fully erect nor totally flaccid.

One prosthesis isn't necessarily better than the others, and a doctor should explain in detail each type of implant available, along with their advantages and shortcomings. Picking a prosthesis is basically a matter of life-style.

"One 72-year-old man I treated enjoys close ballroom dancing every weekend," says Dr. Jaffe. "He wanted the one that would feel the most natural, chose a pump type, and put up with the hassle of inflating because of what was important in his life."

How Satisfying Are Penile Implants?

Surgical implantation of a pair of inflatable rods directly into the penis is an increasingly common solution to chronic, long-term impotence.

How do the recipients of these devices feel about them after months or years of use? "The long-term emotional results vary from sheer delight to frustration, disappointment and outright dislike for the implant," says Fletcher C. Derrick, M.D., clinical professor of urology at the Medical University of South Carolina, Charleston.

In his experience, 85 to 90 percent of patients are very happy with the implant, about 10 percent are somewhat disappointed, and 2 to 5 percent are totally unhappy.

Those who are most gratified, he says, are men who have some sensation in their genitals and at least some erectile capacity left. Those who have had long-term impotence and little or no sensation are likely to be disappointed, Dr. Derrick says, because "an implant does not provide a return of normal sensation and climax." Also, he adds, "Implants almost never achieve the patient's idea of size."

Still, he says, not one of his patients, even those who've expressed the greatest disappointment, has requested that his implant be removed.

The end result of impotence treatment—a restored sex life—is a tremendous relief to both the man and woman who have had to deal with the dilemma. "I've gotten more Christmas cards from former impotency patients than I did in over 20 years of treating cancer patients," notes Dr. Jaffe.

A Problem of Timing

Premature ejaculation can trouble a couple's sex life just as impotence can. With this problem, a man's orgasm catches him off guard: He isn't aware that he is about to climax until it starts happening. When this becomes chronic, self-help or sexual therapy may enable the man to regain control.

The old school of psychosexual thought considered distraction to be the most effective weapon for combating premature ejaculation. The man should get his mind off his arousal, either by counting backward or thinking about baseball or something equally distracting, in order to let an impending orgasm subside and so prolong intercourse. This never really worked, and the updated approach stresses the opposite behavior.

"To increase control, a man must pay particular attention to the sensation in his body as he becomes more and more aroused," says Georgia Witkin-Lanoil, Ph.D., in her book, *The Male Stress Syndrome.* The goal is to recognize premonitory sensations, the body signals that herald the first phase of orgasm, the emission phase. This is when semen arrives in the urethra; ejaculation is only a few seconds away.

If a man tunes in and learns these sensations, "he can slow his thrusting, alter the type of stimulation he is receiving, change position or even pause until control is regained," explains Dr. Witkin-Lanoil, who teaches in the Psychiatry Department of Mount Sinai Medical College in New York.

Enjoying and paying extra attention to arousal can prevent surprise orgasms, and there are some ways to learn this. One is the stop/start technique. A man can stimulate himself until orgasmic sensations begin to build and then stop all movement until the urgency fades. Three cycles of starting and stopping can be followed by an ejaculation. When this is mastered, four, five and six cycles can be practiced, and then done in the same manner with a partner.

Another method is the squeeze technique. This involves both

Even happy, compatible couples can experience sexual problems. The first positive step to getting back into a "honeymoon mode" is communication, both between the partners and with a knowledgeable professional.

partners and a similar cycle theory. "When the man feels his orgasm building, his partner can stop it by firmly squeezing the penis at the base of the tip with her thumb and forefinger," explains sex therapist Bob Kinder, Ph.D., associate professor of psychology in the Clinical and Health Psychology doctoral program at the University of South Florida. Dr. Kinder notes couples have over a 90 percent success rate when they use these methods to overcome premature ejaculation.

Emotional Help for a Woman's Sex Life

Unlike the more tangible devices available to help male sexual problems, treatments for women are usually more along the lines of counseling or psychosexual therapy. This is mostly due to anatomy. The penis is more mechanically complex, and an erection is very visible. In contrast, the primary female response is vaginal lubrication, which is extremely difficult to measure and study scientifically.

If a woman has anxious feelings about herself, her partner or sexual intercourse in general, the negative outlook may show up in her body's physical response to making love. A lack of vaginal lubrication may make sex uncomfortable or even painful; a lack of vaginal cooperation (vaginismus) may make sex impossible.

Stress, minor illness, infections, a mental roadblock, a condition such as diabetes, drugs or advancing age and menopause can all hinder the secretion of lubricating fluid in the vagina. Without it, intercourse can be painful, even making tiny tears in the dry vaginal walls.

For temporary dryness, soothing over-the-counter lubricating jellies can help. But a more extensive problem like the hormonal plunge of menopause may call for an estrogen cream.

"After about three weeks of use," says Albert Altchek, M.D., assistant clinical professor of obstetrics, gynecology and reproductive science at Mount Sinai School of Medicine in New York, "a vaginally inserted estrogen cream can soften, moisten and even thicken the weakened walls of the vagina, as well as reduce any cracks from damaging penile entry. We're even starting to see some evidence that the treatment may help incontinence by improving the urethral walls." (Some women may be at risk for side effects from estrogen, and this cream does get absorbed into the system. A woman's doctor can determine whether she should use the cream.)

Vaginismus, an involuntary spasm of the muscles surrounding the opening of the vagina and the outer third of the vagina, can occur as a reaction to imagined, anticipated or real attempts at penetration.

"The fear of being hurt or injured is a major contributing cause," says noted sex and marital therapist Shirley Zussman, Ed.D., co-director of the Association for Male Sexual Dysfunction. "Organic causes that may produce the pain need to be corrected first, but the roots of vaginismus can often be traced in therapy to an inhibiting background concerning sex.

"Having negative sexual attitudes pounded in by parents since childhood, or too rigidly following the dictates of a strict, disapproving religion are two examples of what can inhibit a woman's sexuality and cause this particular dysfunction," Dr. Zussman says. "Or the reason may be intimacy problems: The woman has trouble trusting others, is emotionally guarded and not sexually responsive."

In any case, the impact of vaginismus can be dramatic. Men may develop impotence when every attempt at making love is futile. It's not unusual for therapists to see clients whose marriages have never been consummated because of it. Leading sex researchers William Masters, M.D., and Virginia Johnson point to an unconsummated marriage in 1 out of every 12 clients they see; Dr. Zussman's estimate of the frequency is similar.

Women used to be labeled frigid when they brought this problem to professional attention. Today the key to treating vaginismus is to help a woman overcome some of her fears and anxieties and learn to relax her vaginal muscle and stretch the vaginal outlet. This is done with physical and psychological approaches.

"Vaginismus is the body reacting to taboos and fears," Dr. Zussman says. "Like the eyes when a finger approaches, it automatically shuts to avoid pain."

A woman can do special exercises to overcome this fear. Therapists have developed a program using dilators in graduated sizes. A woman begins with the smallest-size dilator and, after a warm bath to relax tissues, gently inserts it to stretch the vagina. This is done several times a day, until the largest dilator can be comfortably inserted. Once she can accept her partner doing this to her, she may soon be tolerant of penile insertion. Fingers can be used instead of the dilators.

The other phase of treatment is psychotherapy. "Vaginismus is, after all, the classic example of a psychosomatic condition—the mind has trouble and unconsciously influences the body to react also," notes Dr. Zussman.

The focus in therapy is to give a woman permission to let go and develop new attitudes about herself and her sexuality. Uncovering her past sexual upbringing is a crucial first step.

Basic anatomy education is probably needed in therapy as well, as it was usually withheld from women with vaginismus. Dr. Zussman recalls one woman who, married for eight years without having intercourse, didn't know where her vagina was.

"Both men and women usually do very well and gain a satisfying sex life after therapy," says Dr. Zussman. "Just talking about the sexual problem is therapeutic; for many, it's the first time they've ever talked about it at all. Everyone feels better once they realize a sex problem is not as scary or embarrassing as they had thought. And after this is accomplished, a normal sex life is close at hand."

Understanding Your Mood Calendar

Mary Lamb was, to say the least, moody. The sister of British essayist Charles Lamb was a lovely, literate woman—most of the time. Unfortunately, she was subject to a cyclic psychosis that struck her with uncanny—but predictable—timing. During one of her psychotic attacks, she killed her beloved, ailing mother.

A lawyer friend saved her from prosecution, and she lived a long, relatively normal life between the 38 subsequent attacks. At the first sign of any irritability, her brother would bundle her off to the hospital —or into a straitjacket.

Though most of us experience mood swings less violent than Mary Lamb's, our occasional perplexing moments of grouchiness or euphoria may be just as predictable. There may be a good scientific reason why we get out of the wrong side of the bed on a dark November morning or suffer from languor on a warm spring day. There may be a simple explanation for the workday blues, holiday depression and why a bright sunny day makes us feel that God's in his heaven and all's right with the world.

If gray, gloomy winter days make you feel drab and gloomy, you're not alone. Experts say that the weather has a definite effect on many people's moods.

The answer, as any comic might tell you, is timing. Scientists are just beginning to discover that humans are driven by some silent siren call, like birds that flock and fly south at the first nip of autumn. We're creatures of moods, emotionally influenced by the seasons, the dark of night and light of day and a dependable inner calendar that can remind us—sometimes startlingly—of feelings long forgotten.

As you're about to learn, your sunny disposition probably isn't any more random than your wintertime funk, and that case of spring fever is no run-of-the-mill neurosis. There's a decided advantage to understanding your mood calendar: What you understand is manageable. The calendar, suggests one researcher, may in fact be "our most overlooked yet valuable" diagnostic instrument.

Unhappy Anniversary to You

Evelyn woke up one morning feeling inexplicably disturbed. She blamed her mood on a strange dream she had had—that she was her mother, who died when Evelyn was a child. "I dreamt I was my mother, dying," explains Evelyn, a 35-year-old journalist. "I woke up feeling I had actually experienced death. When I got to work, I told one of my co-workers about the dream, it had been so vivid. Then, as we were about to go for coffee, I began to fill in a financial form to drop off at accounting. As I filled in the date, I suddenly shivered. It was the anniversary of my mother's death 30 years earlier. I hadn't even thought about it before."

Erstwhile psychics might have a field day with Evelyn's experience, but to psychotherapists like Susan Shor of New York, this kind of "anniversary reaction" is quite common.

"In fact, one of the first questions a therapist asks a client who has a sudden deep mood change is, 'What happened to you at this time of year?' People will often experience an emotional change, often unconsciously, uncannily close to the exact date something traumatic has happened to them."

Why? No one really knows, but Shor speculates that unconscious memory keeps better time than conscious thought. Environmental cues —colors of the leaves or smells in the air—may trigger emotional memories, which may explain some seasonal mood changes, including holiday depressions. "September, for instance, may remind of the start of school and the anxiety of meeting new people or missing tests," says Shor.

One theory suggests that these anniversary reactions occur when a dormant unresolved conflict is awakened by what one researcher calls a specific symbolically charged anniversary. Thanksgiving and Christmas—with their patina of family joy and happiness—obviously can be emotionally volatile times for some vulnerable individuals.

Anyone who has ever taken a sudden dislike to a stranger—and ascribed it to "bad vibes"—has probably experienced a close cousin of the anniversary reaction: the transference reaction. Memory is still the key element. "If you really think about it, you realize, 'Oh, yeah, I'm responding to him as if he were so-and-so,' " says Shor.

Unfortunately, these reactions are often inexplicable, at least on the surface. They come unbidden: mysterious dark moods that catch us unawares. To be sure that there's nothing seriously wrong, it can be "very, very helpful," says Shor, to systematically flip through that unconscious calendar whenever we're overcome by out-of-the-blues. We may find that what's bothering us is something we don't remember remembering.

Who's Moodier, Men or Women?

There's no good—or safe—answer to that. Women are often considered moodier because they tend to seem more emotional than men and because of the mood swings associated with the menstrual cycle.

It's true that monthly hormonal changes seem to affect a woman's emotions. In fact, about 60 percent of all women suffer some mild symptoms of premenstrual tension. Some become nervous, weepy and even belligerent. Researchers have found that women the world over—and female primates such as gorillas—share this cyclic "curse."

But what about men? Do they have mood cycles, too? Researchers have found monthly rhythms in the secretions of certain adrenal hormones in male subjects. Two South African scientists, sifting through reports on 2,344 people who contacted a walk-in crisis center, discovered that men tended to have their crisis in the autumn (or during poor economic conditions), while women had theirs in the spring.

One researcher, the late Dr. Rex B. Hershey of the University of Pennsylvania, did a landmark study in 1929-30 that found cyclic fluctuations in the behavior of a group of industrial workers who were otherwise well adjusted.

One man, a 60-year-old who claimed he was strictly even tempered, nevertheless showed evidence of a nine-week cycle. It was so subtle, he never noticed he wasn't as jovial as usual. Another, aged 22, exhibited a cycle roughly equivalent to a menstrual cycle. Another had a four- to six-week cycle characterized by great vigor and confidence in his high periods and lethargy in his low times. He weighed less and slept less during those "high" times.

Let the Sun Shine In

Psychologist Michael Cunningham, Ph.D., may have found scientific evidence for a "sunny disposition." Dr. Cunningham, associate professor of psychology at Elmhurst College in Illinois, found that people tended to be more generous and helpful under sunny skies.

His is one of a number of provocative research projects that suggest the meteorologist might be just as good at predicting our moods as a psychologist. We can literally be "under the weather" on a gray "depressing" day and "hot under the collar" when the mercury soars. One expert estimates that for about two-thirds of us, the weather can have at least a mild effect on our moods.

In Dr. Cunningham's study, experimenters were stationed at four sites in Minneapolis to ask passersby how many of the 80 questions on a survey of social opinions they were willing to answer. He compared the results with readings of sunlight, temperature, barometric pressure, humidity and wind velocity and the phase of the moon on study days.

He found, perhaps not surprisingly, that the nicer the day, the nicer the people. More people were willing to answer more questions on mild sunny days when the temperature was in the mid-70s than on cloudy days when the temperature was higher or lower.

He confirmed those findings in two subsequent studies, one involving the percentage of tips given by restaurant patrons to waitresses and the other on the willingness of motorists to toss money into an unmanned basket at a highway toll plaza. Studies by other researchers have shown that sunshine tends to make people feel "optimistic."

"Sunshine appears to make people pro-social," says Dr. Cunningham. "A positive mood makes us more sensitive to other people. If we're in a negative mood, we're more focused on the task and what we can get out of it. A positive mood anticipates a more positive outcome of our behavior."

What is it about the sun that brings out the best in us? "There are a number of different theories," says the psychologist. "There are those people who believe it's positive memories. A sunny day reminds us of good things that have happened. Cloudy days remind us of ruined plans. Some biologists believe the weather has a direct input, that it stimulates the activity of certain neurochemical pathways. Certain centers of the brain are stimulated by sunlight. Others think we may be wired to respond to the weather. It kept us out of danger. We stayed in our caves in the bad weather. Those who didn't, got caught in a blizzard and didn't live to have children. Or it could be aesthetics. The world just looks prettier in the sun."

Rainy Days and Mondays

Although you may face Monday morning as if it were a firing squad, the traditionally held belief that Monday is the bluest day of the week is not true, according to a study by two psychologists at the State University of New York at Stony Brook.

It just seems that way. In fact, says study director Arthur Stone, Ph.D., when a group of married men were asked to fill out mood reports, it turned out that positive mood was higher Friday through Sunday—understandable because of the positive associations with the weekend. Although mood worsened on Monday, it stayed about the same through Thursday.

That doesn't mean that we consider the week terrible for four out of seven days, cautions Dr. Stone. "It's not quite as good as the weekends, but it's not bad."

Why does Monday have such an undeserved reputation? Probably because mood drops so steeply between Sunday and Monday, a change that is undoubtedly related to the beginning of a new work week. We don't notice much change after that until the weekend arrives again, suggests the psychologist.

Make Mine Light

The winter doldrums and spring fever may have something important in common: light.

Scientists are beginning to suspect that the reduction of the amount of daylight around November and the gradual increase of light around March and April may trigger seasonal depressions in certain susceptible people.

Several important studies have been done by researchers at the National Institute of Mental Health (NIMH), who discovered that they could dramatically alter the moods of patients with serious wintertime depression by exposing them for several hours a day to bright artificial light—effectively creating a spring day in the dead of winter.

This so-called seasonal affective disorder is characterized by sluggishness, depression and a tendency to overeat, oversleep and crave carbohydrates. It appears to be related to a malfunction of the internal clock—what scientists refer to as circadian rhythms. Governing the regular ebb and flow of body chemicals, such as hormones, and even raising and lowering body temperatures at predictable intervals, this clock is "set" in both man and animals by the daily alternation of light and darkness—hence the term *circadian,* meaning "about a day." In animals, light also sets seasonal cycles, triggering hibernation in the fall and signaling mating season at spring thaw. The evidence suggests human cycles may be similarly influenced.

At NIMH, researcher Norman Rosenthal, M.D., and his colleagues have treated a number of patients with a daily dose of bright light—full-spectrum light equivalent to sunlight on a spring day—and found that their moods improved dramatically within two or three days. Ordinary indoor light had no such effect. Prior to this, the only other known cure for these afflicted people was springtime.

April Really Is "the Cruelest Month"

For others, April is, as poet T. S. Eliot observed, "the cruelest month." There are more suicides and more admissions to mental health facilities in early spring than at any other time of the year—giving "spring fever" an ominous meaning.

At the Clarke Institute of Psychiatry in Toronto, M. R. Eastwood, M.D., and his colleagues have been investigating seasonal cycles with a special emphasis on this often-serious spring funk.

In one study, the researchers sorted out by season the number of hospital admissions for mental health reasons over a six-year period in Ontario—representing some quarter of a million patients. They found the greatest number of admissions in the spring, followed by fall. Fewer people were admitted to mental hospitals during the winter.

Later, Dr. Eastwood compared these findings with those of another study in which 30 people with manic-depressive illness—characterized by wide mood swings—kept track of their daily moods for 14 months. A carefully screened control group, with no mental illness, also made daily mood recordings. Both groups had discernible 90-day cycles. The

It's Not the Pale Moon
That Excites Me

Or is it?

Do your moods wax and wane with the moon, or are these "Transylvania" theories sheer lunacy?

Several years ago, Miami psychiatrist Arnold L. Leiber, M.D., garnered national headlines with his provocative book, *The Lunar Effect — Biological Tides and Human Emotions,* in which he showed that violent crime in three cities, including Miami, peaked at the full moon and rose again at the new moon. This confirmed the beliefs of countless police, firefighters and emergency department personnel that the moon inspires aggressive human behavior.

Dr. Leiber's theory: Because we are 80 percent water, there are human biological tides that, like the ocean, are influenced by the moon's pull. A buildup of body water can alter personality, says the psychiatrist. He also suggests that the moon exerts its influence on human behavior through changes in weather, earthquakes and the electromagnetic field.

Since then, other scientists have discounted the theory as, well, loony. Two researchers from Florida International University analyzed 37 published and unpublished studies on the relationship between the moon and human moods. They found that the phases of the moon accounted for no more than 1 percent of the variance in activities termed "lunacy," such as mental hospital admissions and murder.

Other studies, they claim, have been flawed by human error and "a willingness to accept any departure from chance as evidence of a lunar effect."

study found that there was a tendency for people to become clinically depressed during March and April and again during September and October, when the days begin to grow longer and shorter, respectively.

"It's definitely biological," says Dr. Eastwood. "We assume that at these times, their biological clocks get thrown off by the fluctuating sunlight. Those who have a tendency to depression may well get destabilized. Most important, this study showed that these cycles occur in both normals and abnormals. It's a matter of amplitude. Everyone gets destabilized. It's just that the sick get more destabilized."

There is a great potential benefit of this research, Dr. Eastwood believes. "From what we can see, it looks as though mood disorders can be predicted. If they can be predicted," he says, "they can be prevented."

Self-Talk: A New Way to Beat the Blues

You're the last one to squeeze aboard a crowded elevator, but as you begin the slow descent you realize somebody behind you wishes you'd waited for the next one. Whoever is back there is digging a blunt object very firmly and painfully into the small of your back. You're too embarrassed to make a scene, so you just stand there thinking, "I can't believe this! Who *is* that inconsiderate moron back there?"

Finally the elevator touches down on the ground floor and you step off, whirling around quickly to deliver the dirtiest look you can muster. And there stands a white-haired, sweet-faced blind lady, tottering out of the elevator on her cane. Almost instantly, your feelings change to shame and sadness, and you offer her your arm.

It's a story psychologist Robert Reitman, Ph.D., likes to tell to illustrate a profoundly simple point: What you *think* determines how you *feel.* If you want to change your feelings about something, it's almost impossible to simply decide not to feel sad, for instance. But you *can* change you thoughts, and more often than not, your feelings will follow.

And that, in brief, is the fundamental insight behind a school of psychotherapy that's being used with great success to treat depression, anxiety, phobias, drug abuse and other problems that rob life of joy. "Cognitive therapy" is named after its primary subject—your cognitions, or thoughts. A therapist using this approach won't spend a lot of time digging around in the psychic murk of your childhood experiences or dredging up buried associations (a process that can take years, cost a small fortune and produce only questionable results). Instead, cognitive therapists operate in the present, locating and reshaping the thought patterns that are making you anxious, sad, depressed or drug dependent.

Depression: A Thinking Disorder

The technique grew out of the work of Aaron Beck, M.D., a psychiatrist at the University of Pennsylvania who set out during the 1950s to show that Freud was right when he concluded that depression was a disorder caused by turning anger inward. He concluded, after years of study, that Freud was wrong. "I discovered that in their dreams and early memories and in projective tests, depressed people see themselves as 'losers'—deprived, frustrated, rejected, humiliated or punished in some way," Dr. Beck has written. "The psychological 'cause' of depression did not appear to be buried deep in the unconscious but was related to this type of mistaken thinking."

Depression, in short, is a *thinking* disorder. In fact, depression remains a puzzle and a paradox—since it runs directly counter to the human drive for survival—only until you examine a depressed person's thoughts, says Gary Emery, Ph.D., a former student of Dr. Beck's and author of *A New Beginning.* A depressed housewife who feels so overwhelmed by her problems that she stops trying to solve them or can't seem to concentrate on anything except her own flaws, presents a psychological enigma until you discover that she thinks of herself as incompetent, worthless and unlikable. The way to put her back on the road to wellness, Dr. Beck maintains, is by "changing [her] errors in thinking, rather than by concentrating on [her] depressed mood."

Interesting theory, but does it work? "Cognitive therapy has become reputable among professionals very quickly because about 12 studies so far have shown it's as effective or more effective than drugs for depression,"

Dr. Emery says. One recent study at Washington University in St. Louis found that patients treated with cognitive therapy for three months responded just as well as patients treated with tricyclic antidepressants (TCAs), the most commonly prescribed antidepressant drugs. But therapy has one big advantage, observes study leader George Murphy, M.D.: It "has no unpleasant side effects and is absolutely nonfattening."

Faulty Thinking

In many ways, Dr. Emery points out, the notion that emotional problems are caused by faulty thinking isn't new at all, having been recognized a long time ago by early Greek philosophers. Cognitive therapy is "new" in that it has examined and spelled out these thinking errors in greater detail and has developed tools and techniques to alter them.

What are the thinking errors that plague the depressed? Typically, they run along lines like these:

Exaggerating: "I just can't get myself to do any work around the house—my whole marriage is falling apart." You wildly overestimate the size of your problems at the same time you underestimate your ability to deal with them. You jump to conclusions without any evidence and erroneously believe your conclusions are correct.

Ignoring the positive: "Sure the dinner party went all right, but I burned the toast points." You tend to be impressed by and remember only negative events, or view completely positive events in a negative way, often as a way of "proving" the correctness of your negative self-image.

Personalizing: "Everybody at the meeting kept looking at me because I'm gaining weight." You tend to think everything revolves around you—a major distortion of the facts.

Either/or thinking: "Either I get elected head of this committee or I'm a complete failure."

Overgeneralizing: "*Nobody* likes me. . . . I'm losing *all* my friends. . . . *Nothing* ever turns out right. . . . "

As you can see, depressed thoughts begin to sound monotonously alike after a while. That's because they *are* very much alike. For one thing, says Dr. Emery, "the chief characteristic of negative thoughts is that they're generally wrong." They're a distortion or an exaggeration of the truth. That's at least partly because they tend to be *automatic.* That is, they simply leap into your mind unbidden; they're not conclusions you've reached through reason and logic. In fact, in a sense they're not "thinking" at all.

How do "thought therapists" go about reshaping these negative, self-defeating, soul-saddening thought patterns? Not just by serving up a reheated version of "the power of positive thinking," Dr. Emery says. "In positive thinking you're replacing one global judgment ('I'm no good') for another ('I'm wonderful')," he says, and *neither* is realistic. As social philosopher Max Lerner has observed, "To believe either that everything is bound to work out or that nothing will ever work out is equally an exercise in mindlessness." The point is to put your life and your problems in a *realistic* perspective. Like a reporter, a scientist or a detective, you're looking to find the true facts of the case, to apply the principles of hard science to your own thought processes.

The plan of attack is in three phases, Dr. Emery says: awareness, answering and action.

Awareness: The First Phase

Vague, unfocused negative thoughts that lurk just below the surface of consciousness cause more harm than those that are dragged out into the open. So the first step out of the rut of depression is to become *aware* of what you're actually thinking and feeling.

Sometimes that's more difficult than it sounds, since these thoughts tend to be well disguised. Dr. Emery suggests using a sort of "instant replay" technique, thinking back to what crossed your mind just before a mood change or a physical sensation such as fatigue, heaviness or butterflies in the stomach. Sometimes there *is* no preceding thought— you only later attribute a certain thought ("I'm worthless") to a certain feeling (sadness), says Arthur Freeman, Ed.D., a therapist at the Center for Cognitive Therapy at the University of Pennsylvania. "But whichever comes first, the thought or the feeling, we still find cognitive intervention effective," Dr. Freeman says.

Another way to become more aware of your negative thoughts is simply to count them. You can use a plastic grocery-store price counter or a small stitch counter (sold in knitting shops) or just transfer coins (a penny is one thought, a dime ten thoughts) from one pocket to another. "These gimmicks remind you to become aware of your thinking," Dr. Emery says. "You discover that you have the same thoughts over and over again."

"It's important to 'concretize' vague, negative thoughts," agrees Dr. Freeman. "One of the simplest ways is to write them down. We try to help patients separate thoughts into three distinct aspects: what the situation is, what you're feeling about it and what you're saying to yourself [your thoughts]."

Most of us don't consider situations objectively; instead we load them up with all kinds of projections and judgments, Dr. Freeman says. You may think, for instance, "I'm waiting for my girlfriend to call me, but she probably won't because she knows I'm a loser." The first step is to strip away everything except the plain, simple facts: "I'm waiting for my girlfriend to call." Period. Next you sift your experience in search of your true feelings. "The first thing you come up with may be, 'I feel like a loser,' but I submit that's not a feeling, that's a thought," Dr. Freeman says. "Then it's 'I feel as if she'll never call'—again, not a feeling, a thought. Finally you get to 'I feel sad.' Okay—*that's* the feeling."

Then you've got to tune in to your self-talk concerning the situation. Why have you concluded your girlfriend isn't going to call? If she's late, has it ever happened before? What other reasonable explanations are there to account for the fact that she's late calling? In short, Dr. Freeman says, you've got to *examine the evidence.* You've got to drag your negative thoughts into court, put them on the witness stand and confront them with the facts. Usually, they'll wilt under the pressure.

Dr. Emery, when counseling a woman who was depressed because she believed no man would ever want to marry a divorcée with two children, told her to go to the library and look up the statistics. She found that women with children were actually *more* likely to find new mates than childless single women of the same age.

Answering Negative Thoughts

Once you've identified and clarified the thought patterns that are making you feel bad, you've got to answer them. One of the best ways to pry open the closed circle of negative thoughts is to learn to ask yourself good questions. Become a hard-nosed prosecutor and grill your negative thoughts but good. What's the evidence that I'm such a worthless person? Am I confusing a mere thought with a fact? Am I overlooking my strengths? Exactly what is the distortion in my thinking? Am I exaggerating or overgeneralizing? And so on.

A good way to clarify this process for yourself, Dr. Beck suggests, is to divide a piece of paper into two columns and write out a more balanced, fact-based, realistic answer beside each recurrent negative thought. A gloomy, lonesome housewife may think, "I'm neglected because nobody wants to be around me." But in the opposite column, if she gave it a little thought, she could answer, "Mary hasn't called because she's in the hospital, Judy is out of town and Helen really *did* call but I forgot about that."

Occasionally, Dr. Emery says, you may be so upset that no reasonable answer comes immediately to mind. So postpone answering—wait an hour or two or set aside a certain time each day to write out your answers. One of his patients, expanding on this idea, created a "Wednesday box" in which she deposited all her thoughts and ideas that bothered her during the week. On Wednesdays, she opened the box, tore up the thoughts that were no longer a problem and tried to constructively answer those that still were.

Taking Action for a Better Life

It's not enough to simply answer your negative thoughts—you have to act on your new thoughts and beliefs. In a way, Dr. Emery points out, acting out your written answers to negative, self-defeating thoughts is a way of "reality testing" them to see if they're really true. How do you know for sure that you "can't" speak in public unless you try it? Or that you'll be rejected if you introduce yourself to someone you're attracted to? (It's possible you really can't speak in public, and you really will be rejected—but you'll never know until you try.)

For people mired in the deep mud of depression, Dr. Beck suggests working up an activity schedule or a weekly calendar with each day divided into hour-long boxes. The idea is to schedule something throughout the day and keep a record of how well you did with each task—

perhaps by rating on a scale of one through five the amount of pleasure or sense of accomplishment it gave you.

This simple little calendar can help in many ways. It gives you the true facts about what you actually do during the day—demonstrating to many depressed people that their lives aren't as bleak or empty as they had imagined. It helps you retake control of your life by breaking the rut of inactivity. And it helps you see clearly what gives you pleasure and satisfaction.

A Skill, Not a Cure

By becoming *aware* of your negative thoughts, *answering* them with a more realistic, constructive and adaptive view, and taking *action* to break out of your self-imposed trap, you can get control of depression and anxiety. But can you ever be cured? "Cognitive therapy is a skill-building process—we're not talking about cures," Dr. Freeman explains. "Some patients call back in a year or so and ask to come in again for a kind of 'booster' session. But they've learned skills to help them cope, and their relapses tend to be fewer and shorter."

Do you need a therapist at all? "Thirty-five or 40 years ago, when the first psychological self-help books came out, there was a hysterical cry from the public and the profession alike that, 'You can't do it that way! You can't help yourself!' " says Dr. Reitman, a therapist who doubles as president of PSYCOMP, a California computer software company that's producing cognitive therapy computer programs to treat problems ranging from stress to sexual dysfunction. "But now we know that people have a great capacity to help themselves with psychological problems. And cognitive therapy, because it deals with thoughts, is especially suited to books, articles, tapes and computer programs. This is not *therapy,* mind you, but these things can really help, if people choose to help themselves."

Building Self-Esteem

The blues are like a natural warning gauge. They're usually set off by our losses and letdowns and flash a signal that something is wrong. It may take a little time, but most of us bounce back from the blues and continue our course of living.

Sometimes, though, our inner gauge gets stuck, heading us straight for depression. And that's a dead-end condition, one that affects 25 percent of all people—most of them women—during their lifetime.

How do women arrive at that emotionally unhealthy destination? Look closely and you'll probably find very low levels of self-esteem. Psychotherapist Linda Tschirhart Sanford, coauthor with Mary Ellen Donovan of *Women and Self-Esteem,* says that your level of self-esteem comes from how much you value your image of yourself. And with women that value is often low—so low, in fact, that when the women interviewed for the book were asked what they liked about themselves, many could not come up with one single answer!

It seems that women with low self-esteem have certain problems in common no matter what their differences in age, race, income level or occupation, says Sanford. When asked how they valued themselves, women responded that they thought of themselves as "blank," or else they said it didn't matter if they had a self at all! Others defined themselves as total failures, and still more discounted their successes.

Then, too, women with self-esteem problems said they felt they weren't the person they used to be (that particular self-esteem crisis often follows a change involving loss—like mastectomy or divorce). Finally, women who were facing life-style decisions, like the switch from career to motherhood or vice versa, acknowledged that they felt uncertain about who they should be.

Sound familiar? That's because these are common attitudes among women raised in the traditional structure of our society and families, says Sanford. For most women, self-esteem was often not high on the list of lessons to be learned as little girls. When it comes to changing these attitudes, though, the responsibility is yours, and the sooner you switch to a higher level of self-esteem, the more equipped you will be to make a detour around depression.

Yet depression may not be the only thing to worry about. True

(continued on page 36)

Many women who suffer from depression are victims of low self-esteem. Learning to see themselves in a more positive way can brighten their outlook and lift their spirits.

Roadblocks to Self-Esteem

See if you can find yourself in these descriptions, adapted from *Women and Self-Esteem,* by Linda Tschirhart Sanford and Mary Ellen Donovan.

The Black Clouder

Negative thinking: A clerk is rude, and you conclude it must be because of something you did. You blow up passing comments and opinions into attacks on your overall self-worth. You mindread and react to supposed judgments.

Solution: Get clarification and check out assumptions whenever possible. Otherwise, decide it's the other person's problem. If you think, "Why was that clerk so rude to me; what's wrong with me?" *stop.* Replace it with, "I have no way of knowing what's on her mind. It doesn't have anything to do with me."

The Perfectionist

Negative thinking: You think in if-then terms. "If I work and do this job perfectly, then I will be worthwhile." You use a lot of shoulds. You believe you must be best in all areas—and you are perpetually dissatisfied, since nothing ever is perfect. You think failure is evidence of your worthlessness, so you take few risks.

Solution: Begin to notice the importance the media and our culture give to the illusion of perfection (perfect wife, perfect businesswoman, perfect hostess). Write out your own if-then scheme. Is it realistic? Can you live without it? Choose only three specific areas in which you'd like to excel. If you're obsessed with being perfect, try thought-stopping. Replace it with, "I'm giving this my most sincere effort. What's important is that I enjoy it while I'm trying."

The Chronic Comparer

Negative thinking: Someone enters the room and you conclude that "She is more fit, but I'm smarter." You always look for differences in everyone and how you rank. Usually you come out inferior and feel envy. You make hasty judgments without adequate information, and you wind up feeling guilty.

Solution: Ask yourself if you were ever compared to others, perhaps a sibling, as a child. Compare yourself only to yourself. Or ask, "So what?" (Don't give an answer. Instead switch to a value-neutral thought like vacation planning.) If you think, "She seems so happy in that relationship. I'm sure a jerk, I'll never have a relationship like that," *stop.* Replace it with, "Well, maybe it will happen to me someday, too."

The Conditional Lover

Negative thinking: You feel worthy only under certain conditions . . . when you have the right relationship or job or when you have a child. You believe your existence is validated only by someone or something outside yourself. You are unable to accept aloneness, and you keep searching for something to give you meaning.

Solution: Reverse your if-then thoughts. Think "If I love myself, then I will be more able to successfully love another person." Balance work, relationship and fun activities. Realize that your self-worth starts within. Learn to be alone—find a safe, quiet place (like a bench) to be alone without talking or distractions.

The Poor Body-Imager

Negative thinking: You inaccurately see yourself as being dominated by thunder thighs, wide hips, big feet, sagging breasts or a big nose. Your body image is distorted, and you feel somewhat alienated from it. You are your most severe critic.

Solution: Ask what labels you were given as a child. Be aware of our cultural stereotype for women's bodies. Ask yourself if your image of yourself is real or distorted.

Study your own body in detail in a mirror. Look around the locker room and see that women come in all shapes and sizes.

depression is disruptive; it can disturb sleep, numb feelings, even encourage thoughts of suicide. That kind of depression requires professional evaluation and treatment.

More often, what many women call depression turns out to be a catchall name for other kinds of feelings. "It may be a safer or more comfortable term to admit to than being sad, despairing, worried, restless or bored," says Sanford. "Somehow, many women find it more acceptable to be 'depressed.'"

The one emotion women often have the hardest time identifying and expressing is anger. Yet depression is often anger turned inward, reminds psychiatrist Helen A. DeRosis, M.D., author of *The Book of Hope.*

Call it what you will, most experts today say depression is learned. "That means it can be unlearned," says Sanford.

Think Your Way Out

Perhaps the greatest boon for chronic blues sufferers is cognitive therapy, the popular drug-free, couchless way to climb out of the dumps. Cognitive therapy is based on the idea that moods are linked to thoughts. Change your thoughts, and you'll change your moods. "It's an effective way to think your way out of depression and gain control over your life," explains George Murphy, M.D., director of outpatient psychiatry, Washington University School of Medicine.

Sanford applies many cognitive therapy techniques in helping women overcome low self-esteem and diffuse depression, except she takes it one step further. "It's important for women to remember that their origins of low self-esteem are not just in their heads," she says. "Our culture and upbringing have had a lot to do with where we are emotionally today."

So while her treatment program focuses on how women can change negative thinking patterns that perpetuate low self-esteem, she also encourages them to question how they learned such thinking and to be aware of how it might be reinforced in society.

Five Ways to Manage Moods

Changing your thoughts is one good way to head off depression, but it's not the only way. "In order to really diagnose depression and treat it effectively," says Carol Nadelson, M.D., the first woman to be elected president of the American Psychiatric Association, "we need to consider the total picture. Women—and their doctors—should take a closer look at life-style habits that may be part of the problem."

Changing those habits can also be part of the cure for depression. Here are five ways to help you steer clear of those low-down feelings.

Get up and go.   When you feel like moping, do something—anything. Try cleaning a drawer, which will help give you a sense of accomplishment and build your self-esteem. Physical exercise—especially aerobic activities—has been shown to have a significant antidepressant effect if done three times a week for at least 30 minutes.

Make contact with people you care about.   You may not feel like socializing, but others can help to distract you from your depression, give you hugs, listen to you and even help you have fun.

Start smiling.   Studies show that your smile muscles send the same positive signals to your nervous system as when you are actually happy.

Avoid drugs, including alcohol.   Any drug may depress the central nervous system and keep you feeling down.

Relax!   Try progressive relaxation techniques or yoga exercises, which are known to reduce stress, counteract depression and promote well-being as well as help you sleep.

New Clues to Baby Blues

Postpartum depression affects more than 80 percent of all new mothers and causes a wide range of problems, from the mild letdown occurring after delivery to more serious and longer-lasting symptoms of feeling worthless and hopeless. Until recently, few women admitted their postpartum depression.

"Women have been commonly viewed as a little bit crazy when they're going through changes like pregnancy and menopause," says Dyanne Affonso, Ph.D., associate professor and coordinator of perinatal nursing, University of California.

Dr. Affonso hopes to identify the symptoms of postpartum depression to determine if it can be treated as a syndrome, separate from other psychological disorders. She also hopes to continue researching the causes.

"The traditional hormone and personality theories are incomplete," says Dr. Affonso. For example, all mothers have a change in hormones, but only *some* experience depression. Furthermore, it's often difficult to measure personality traits said to trigger the depression.

What we must look at, she believes, are psychological factors— things like the mother's relationship with the father, her social networks, how much help she gets for child care, whether she is changing her life-style from a career and how isolated she is from other supportive adults.

"Women continue to fall through the cracks of care. Except for the standard six-week checkup, pediatrics pick up where obstetrics leave off," says Dr. Affonso. She wants to see postpartum as part of obstetric care that continues well past six weeks. Depression could then be resolved early, before it affects the mother's (and baby's) life later on.

In the meantime, it is possible to prevent many postpartum problems by joining a support group. "Our program believes that preparing for parenting is more than obstetricals and learning how to breathe," says Maureen Finnerty Turner, executive director of the Boston-based COPE (Coping with the Overall Pregnancy/Parenting Experience). Turner suggests you include these things in your pregnancy plans.

- Learn progressive relaxation so you can sleep better (when you do snatch some sleep time).
- Arrange for help with housework and child care ahead of time.
- Find out if you can have flexible hours or shorten your workday until at least six months after your baby's birth.
- Line up an experienced mother or group of people to talk to.
- Plan something just for yourself daily—soak in the tub or play a tape on your Walkman. Make sure you and the baby get outside as much as you can.
- Decide to maintain some outside interests, even if it's just through phone calls.
- For the parenting support group nearest you, contact the Family Resource Coalition, 230 N. Michigan Avenue, Chicago, IL 60601 (312) 726-4750.

Turn Off Your Tension Center

Does life give you a *real* pain in the neck? Does tension build slowly in your shoulders during the day until they feel like they're reinforced with concrete? Have your neck and shoulders become your "tension center"?

You're not alone. Most of us do things every day—at work, at home and at play—that inject tension into the muscles of our neck and shoulders. We literally shoulder our burdens, both physical and emotional.

"I call it carrying the weight of the world on your shoulders," says Susan L. Fish, a registered physical therapist in New York City. "It's the second most common problem that I see, after low back pain."

If you're feeling a lot like Atlas these days, don't despair. You may be able to cast off your burden simply by changing some of your tension-toting habits.

"One major cause of neck and shoulder pain is a round-shouldered posture," Fish says. "It throws the head forward and leaves us looking down. But we tend to want to see where we're going, so we arch our head back. Holding our head up in that forward-jutting position puts a tremendous amount of stress on the muscles in the back of the neck and upper shoulders. And a muscle that's in a constant state of contraction can become a painful muscle.

"Part of the problem is habit. Part is genetic. Part is just generally poor posture, from the feet all the way up. For instance, large-busted women may get round-shouldered because of the weight of their breasts. In postmenopausal women, osteoporosis can contribute to it. And fatigue can cause you to be round-shouldered because people who don't get enough sleep just can't hold themselves up straight."

Slouching in your easy chair is another way to make your neck and shoulders uneasy. "If you let yourself scoot down in your chair and slouch in your lower back, you're going to go into that round-shouldered

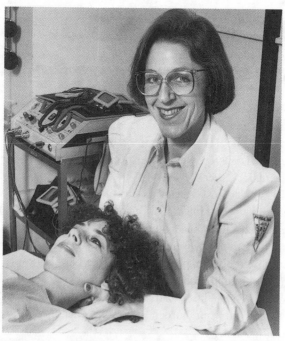

Susan L. Fish, a registered physical therapist in New York City, applies manual traction to relieve muscle spasm in the neck and shoulders—the "tension center"—of a client.

posture," says Fish. "One of the best ways to avoid that is to support your lower back. When you sit right up on the base of your buttocks with a support in your lower back, it's hard to slouch over. Lumbar-support chairs are helpful for that reason."

Putting yourself in the driver's seat can also throw you out of alignment. "Many automobile seats are designed to allow you to slouch down," Fish points out. "Again, I recommend that my patients use back supports and sit erect. But I don't want to minimize the fact that I give all of my patients with neck and shoulder pain an individualized exercise program geared to strengthening the upper back muscles, stretching the inner chest muscles and maintaining a posture where the spine is straight."

Don't Look Down

People who constantly look down at their work are going to strain the neck and shoulders, too. "After about an hour of working at my computer terminal, my shoulders and neck would begin to ache," recounts David Rosenkrantz, an engineer. "The pain would get worse as the day went on: I'd get so uncomfortable that I couldn't concentrate. I had to do something, so one day I tried raising the monitor. That alleviated most of the stiffness. It turns out that because I'm tall, I was constantly looking down to read the screen."

"It's common for typists and people who work at computers to have neck and shoulder pain," says Fish. "Typists should use a book stand to copy from rather than laying the source flat on the desk. And computer users should have the screen at eye level," she advises. "That will keep them from constantly tiring those neck muscles."

If you're having trouble reading the fine print these days, you could be sticking your neck out. "Nearsighted people often jut their heads forward so they can see better," Fish says. "That can also cause neck and shoulder pain. Corrective lenses should take care of it, if the person has not already developed the habit of leaning forward."

Reading in bed with your head propped up on a tower of pillows can also put a kink in your neck. Your chest, it seems, is a poor choice for a chin rest. Fish recommends using angled pillows that hold the head straight but elevate the whole upper body.

Excess Baggage

Could your shoulder bag carry the U.S. mail? Could your briefcase anchor the Queen Mary? Carrying a heavy load continually on one side will almost certainly make your neck and shoulders cry uncle. "One day I was carrying a heavy shoulder bag when I went shopping," recalls Ellen Moser, a housewife. "Hours later I got a funny feeling in my neck. I thought it was nothing. But when I woke up the next morning it was terribly painful. So I went to the emergency room at a local hospital. The doctor who saw me figured out that the pain was from carrying a heavy shoulder bag.

"The pain lasted for about six weeks and kept me up at night. It took a long time to heal, but it eventually went away. I just made sure to not carry the shoulder bag for any length of time. And if I was going shopping, I unloaded everything except the necessities—like money."

"When you carry a heavy shoulder bag or briefcase, you wind up with your body tilted over," explains Fish, "but you hold your head upright so you can see straight. So one side of your neck is constantly contracted. The muscle never totally relaxes. If you have to carry heavy things, divide the weight evenly between both of your arms. If you must wear a shoulder bag, switch sides occasionally. And if at all possible, try not to use one at all."

Even an everyday activity like talking on the telephone can call up pain in your muscles. "Holding a telephone between your ear and your shoulder really contributes to keeping those upper shoulder muscles in a constant state of tension. People who do that habitually should get either a phone rest or a headset," Fish recommends.

To a large extent, neck and shoulder problems are side effects of twentieth-century life. The causes—using a computer, talking on the telephone, carrying a briefcase—are also related to the *pace* of modern man.

Please Release Me

"Every time something upsets you or you feel aggravated, your body tenses up," explains Dennis T. Jaffe, Ph.D., professor of psychology at Saybrook Institute in San Francisco and coauthor of *From Burnout to Balance.* "It's part of the body's reaction to anything that's threatening. Your muscles tense up, your breathing gets shallower, you secrete adrenaline, and your whole body gets thrown into overdrive. That's what the stress response is.

"The problem is that most of the things that are upsetting to us do not require that kind of response. It's inappropriate to respond physically even though your body is responding physically. And if you don't do something to release the muscle tension, it stays there, even after the upset is over. Your body doesn't rebound to normal. So, over the course of a day, muscle tension builds up. Many people have a tendency to hold that tension in their neck and shoulders.

"Physically active people definitely have less trouble with it," Dr. Jaffe points out, "because they're out there releasing their muscles all the time. But people who are sitting all day, especially if they're hunched over, need to find ways to release the tension."

If your shoulders are nearly touching your ears, that's a clue that you're holding tension in them. "I sometimes have patients look in the mirror, then I tell them to drop their shoulders. Some people drop them about three inches," says Fish. "When they see it in the mirror, they become aware of the fact that their shoulders were almost touching their earlobes. It's really an education. Many people don't even know that they're doing it.

"I find that the most beneficial thing to recommend is axial extension, or elongating the neck. To do that, look straight ahead, keeping your chin parallel to the floor. Imagine that your head is being pulled straight up. When you do axial extension, you're forced to relax the muscles in your shoulders and drop them down. The result is correct posture.

"The one thing I usually would not do," says Fish, "is give patients a cervical collar unless there is a neurological problem as well. If they wear a collar, they'll weaken their muscles. I don't use collars for this kind of muscle tension problem."

But there are many other things you can do to help relax those muscles. "Letting a hot shower run on the back of your neck is probably one of the most effective ways to relax the neck and shoulder muscles," says Paul J. Rosch, M.D., president of the American Institute of Stress in Yonkers, New York.

"Progressive muscle relaxation exercises are also very helpful. To do them, you progressively tense then relax the different muscle groups in your body. For example, you may start with your hands, then tense and relax your forearms, then your upper arms, then your shoulders and so on. That's one technique that's used by a variety of practitioners to relax muscles and reduce stress. Deep breathing seems to help, too."

Breaking the Cycle

More serious cases may benefit from professional attention. "When a muscle goes into spasm, sometimes it sets up a vicious circle," Dr. Rosch points out. "It may contract down on the nerve that carries the sensation of the pain. If it does that, the nerve becomes irritated, which causes continued muscle spasm. In some instances it's possible to break the cycle by injecting an anesthetic to release the spasm. When the spasm is reduced, there's no longer any pressure on the nerve and you break the cycle. Pain-relieving, anti-inflammatory and muscle-relaxant drugs can also be effective if they break the spasm/pain cycle.

"However," cautions Dr. Rosch, "if you have persistent pain that used to be relieved by simple analgesics like aspirin and no longer is, that's a sign that you should see a physician. You should also seek medical attention if you have numbness or tingling in your arms or fingers, pain down your arms or changes in the muscle tone in your arms or hands."

"I treat a lot of this muscle spasm with electrical stimulation," says Fish. "That's the use of electricity to stop the muscle spasms. Some people use ultrasound as well. The deep heat it creates increases the circulation."

"When a muscle is tense, the flow of blood can be cut off," says Marilyn Frender, licensed massage therapist in New York City and editor of the *American Massage Therapy Association Journal.* "Massage can increase circulation, warming the muscles and taking out tension. It can soothe and relax the muscles as well as calm the person. It's good for general body relaxation and stress reduction.

"You don't need to be an expert, either. You can help someone relax their shoulders by running your hands smoothly from the nape of the neck across the shoulders, stroking toward the heart. There are seminars available in many cities that teach self-massage and massage for couples. Or if you prefer, you can try to locate medical practitioners or health clubs."

"The important thing," says Dr. Rosch, "is to recognize where the sources of stress are in your life that might be causing this."

Dr. Jaffe agrees. "Anything that's upsetting or creates conflict in your life can give you tension. It's important to look at the stress in your life and make changes. If you release the tension but keep going back into the same kind of stress, you'll just keep creating problems for yourself."

Helping Your Child Cope

If Jessie had been able to talk, she would have protested loudly: "What are you doing? This is my room! Leave my stuff alone!" But Jessie's only two, and her protests came in the form of crying, whining and clinging. Her parents, who were trying to move things out of her bedroom to make room for new furniture, just wanted to get the job done; they were in no mood to deal with Jessie's tantrum.

An understanding aunt came to the little girl's aid. She said: "I think Jessie's upset because her room is being dismantled. She doesn't know what's happening; she's probably afraid of being abandoned. Let's try to find some way to reassure her." And sure enough, once the parents looked at their daughter's behavior from *Jessie's* perspective, they were able to be compassionate about her tears and fears and help her deal with a situation that was stressful for her.

Defining Stress

Stress refers to what happens when a threat or challenge or conflict puts us on tilt, and children aren't immune to the stress created by change. The problem is, parents may not recognize temper tantrums and other "bad behavior" exhibited by children for what they are—childish (but normal) reactions to stress. The task is to learn what's stressful to your child. "The main criterion is unpredictable events, the disruption of a predictable routine," says Elaine Dolch, an assistant professor of child development at Purdue University in West Lafayette, Indiana, and director of the Purdue Child Care Program.

The causes—psychologists call them stressors—can be positive, like getting a great report card or anticipating an upcoming trip. More often we think of them as negative—an F in algebra. In either case, we adapt to regain balance.

Stress also triggers physical reactions. Television ads have made the tension headache—exemplified by a harried woman clutching her painful head—a cliché for what scientists call the stress response.

Though they may not be able to express it verbally, children feel that response, too. In one study, second-graders excreted significantly higher levels of a hormone associated with stress on achievement-test days than on normal days, according to researchers at the University of Colorado.

Certain normal stress is built into childhood, forming a sort of obstacle course mapped by nature over time and set with a multitude of hurdles.

"The environment places a lot of barriers for little people—high drinking fountains, high doorknobs—all sources of frustration. The older a child gets, the more he ventures into a wider environment with more opportunities for stress," says Peter J. Behrens, Ph.D., psychologist and assistant professor at Pennsylvania State University's Allentown campus.

Separation from family is a major source of stress for young children, especially anxiety that accompanies the first weeks of school or day care, adds Susan Leibmann, M.D., director of outpatient services for children, adolescents and families at Thomas Jefferson University Hospital in Philadelphia and assistant professor at Jefferson Medical College.

"At ages four and five, their life is their family. They are susceptible to anything that disrupts it," she says. "For school-age children there are new demands. They have to perform cognitively. They have a new authority figure, a teacher, and they have peers to get along with."

Preadolescent years may bring the stress of growth, sexual maturation and rigorous academic demands. "There is more concern with what peers have to say and a constant struggle trying to separate from the family. Separating—developing one's goals and priorities, in school and among peers—is a big issue," Dr. Leibmann says.

Change Brings Emotional Upheavals

Psychologist David Elkind, Ph.D., professor at Tufts University in Medford, Massachusetts, and author of *The Hurried Child,* blames our fast-paced age for contributing to the stressors kids face.

We have changed from an industrial to a service economy, Dr. Elkind says. The computer is replacing the smokestack. "That's all in direct contrast to what we were in the last 40 years. Whenever you have a society in transition, you have stress. The stresses today are psychological. When social values change, that's the worst time for children."

Change has invaded family life, too. The divorce rate has more

School performance—both academic and social—is one of the most common stresses that children must deal with. Parents should be careful to set realistic goals for their children and to be available when problems arise.

than doubled since 1960, according to government statistics. And more than 24.5 million American kids age 13 and under now have working mothers, compared to 19.5 million a decade ago, according to the U.S. Bureau of Labor Statistics.

"There are a lot of [career] pressures on parents, on women," continues Dr. Elkind. "When parents are stressed, they unfortunately stress kids. You see the same thing in teachers. It's a whole chain of causation."

In his book, Dr. Elkind chronicles how youngsters are rushed with an adult agenda. Ballet lessons, soccer practice and computer camp preempt neighborhood games of kick-the-can and sandlot baseball.

Anyone shopping for kids' clothes can see the evidence. One popular children's store sells bikini panty and bra sets — for four-year-olds.

In a curious role reversal, parents struggling with layoffs and divorces turn to children as confidants, imposing more responsibility than youth should carry. "Kids feel unparented because parents are not taking the responsibility they should," Dr. Elkind says.

Spotting the Signs

In most settings, it takes a perceptive parent or teacher to spot what a child is unable or unwilling to express. Children signal distress with symptoms that may develop in subtle or dramatic ways, then persist in four areas described by Dr. Leibmann.

Emotional functioning.   Trouble here can take many forms, like continual crying or whining, a sense of hopelessness, a worried outlook.

Behavior.   A child might become withdrawn, aggressive or irritable. In older children, Dr. Leibmann says, these symptoms could be reflected in truancy, fighting with peers or stealing.

School performance.   Children overwhelmed by stress have difficulty paying attention and doing homework. Their grades drop.

Health.   When stress bothers children, symptoms can be physical — headaches, insomnia, appetite changes, asthma. Parents should heed these complaints, Dr. Leibmann points out.

Steeled against Stress

In spite of what appears to be a bleak picture, research offers a hopeful outlook. Pioneering work at the University of Minnesota in Minneapolis lends insight into what steels children against stress.

It's part of Project Competence, an ongoing 15-year investigation directed by Norman Garmezy, Ph.D., a psychology professor at the university. Early research focused on children who were having trouble adjusting to stress and those considered at risk because of parental disorders.

The project more recently has focused on 200 children from a normal elementary school setting. Researchers also have studied resilience —reflected in competent social and school performance—among youngsters with congenital heart defects and severely physically handicapped children faced with being mainstreamed into regular public school classes.

"Despite the stressfulness of our world, most children manage to come through it," Dr. Garmezy says. "The majority are able to overcome the disadvantages they labor under."

But how?

Dr. Garmezy points to three factors that appear to shape well-adjusted, able children.

- Positive personality traits, such as being bright and responsive. Intelligent children are good at problem solving, a basic coping skill, he explains. A responsive child is good at enlisting adult help.
- A warm, supportive family. A parent helps "inoculate" a child against stress by nurturing him and encouraging self-direction. "Family" does not necessarily mean an intact family, Dr. Garmezy emphasizes. "We have many single-parent families who have these attributes." What is vital is that the parent maintain the family's cohesion and stability, where parent and child have responsibilities appropriate to their roles.
- Support from outside the family. Teachers, for example, give children vital skills and reinforce self-esteem. "Our work would lead me to say that the first necessity of a school is to teach competence, in the form of social and cognitive skills, for these qualities are needed when a person is under stress," Dr. Garmezy says.

What You Can Do

Your response to situations that are stressful for your children is important in determining how *they* will handle things. Being supportive and understanding may be difficult at times, but it will bring positive results.

Show your child you love him, no matter what.
This sounds obvious. It may not be so obvious when your six-year-old has splashed a quart of apple juice on the floor, the wall and himself . . . and you are already late for work.

A hug, offered with reassurance that these things happen, has curative powers that make mopping the floor and apologizing to the boss all worthwhile. Psychologists point to a loving parent as a child's most invincible armor.

Adults also need to share themselves. "Parents sometimes go for the big experience with children instead of just making dinner together," comments Purdue's Elaine Dolch. "What the child needs is that quiet, relaxed time to stay in touch socially and emotionally."

Be honest.
Teachers, nurses and therapists emphasize that children need straight answers in language they understand.

"Children don't like to find out you've lied to them," says Lois Trouland, a registered nurse who prepares children for orthopedic surgery at the Philadelphia unit of Shriners Hospitals. "If you lie, you lose their confidence."

Master little stressors first.
"Parents can use everyday stressors to advantage by gradually introducing them—little bites as opposed to big chunks. In that way, children can adapt when big stressors come along," says Penn State's Dr. Behrens.

Taking the school bus to kindergarten, for example, is a stressful situation that parents can transform into an opportunity for mastery. Anxiety usually centers around missing the bus. Knowing that it is the nature of a five-year-old to take half the morning to find his pants, a parent might ease the tension by locating them the night before.

Parents need to be understanding. "Say the child misses the bus. The parents shouldn't increase stress by getting very angry," says Dr. Behrens. "Parents who are supportive are also the ones who can deal

Supportive parents who are willing to listen compassionately to their children's problems can help ease some of the stresses that children face.

with stress. If parents have learned how to deal with time pressure, they most likely can teach their child to deal with it, too."

Keep in touch with how your child feels.   The time to deal with stress is before it sets up a vicious circle of behavior or school problems.

"It means asking children directly about how they feel and what they're thinking. I recommend the 'what if' question," says Dr. Behrens. "Put the child in a hypothetical situation so he can work it through."

Parents also need to be alert to physical problems, such as poor vision or hearing, that add stress to schoolwork and other daily activities.

Be consistent.   Fred Boccella, who counsels junior high school children in the Philadelphia school system, watches wearily when parents send conflicting cues.

"You get two parents and neither knows what the other is doing. The father says one thing, the mother the opposite. The child is getting mixed signals. He's confused. He comes to school angry and has a poor self-image. He's restless, inattentive and a poor achiever." Set limits and stick with them, the counselor says.

Set goals within reach.   Adults whose expectations exceed a child's timetable or abilities—insisting on early reading or entrance to an advanced scholastic program a pupil doesn't belong in, for example —ask for trouble.

"The child begins to view himself as inadequate and not as good as another child," says Boccella. A far better approach is to nurture strengths.

Recognize the value of play.   Play, without direct parental supervision, is filled with learning and exploration. It lets children try new roles. They learn at their own pace, free of adult criticism, and work out relationships with peers.

"Children are shoved into a lot of activities in the guise of giving them a full life," observes Dolch. Parents need to ask themselves who really benefits from these activities.

Dealing with Your Child's Sleep Problems

If you have never been hassled by bedtime battles, wails from the nursery when you're in a deep sleep, midnight nudges to "move over, Mommy, I'm coming in," sleep terrors or nightmares, then you're probably not a parent.

Sleep problems in children, it seems, come with the territory. Frequently they cause tremendous worry, anger, fatigue and frazzled nerves. Your enjoyment of their childhood is diminished by your longing for the day they will grow out of it.

It doesn't have to be that way. Most sleep disorders can be corrected, usually in less than two weeks and without trauma to parent or child, maintains Richard Ferber, M.D., director of the Center for Pediatric Sleep Disorders at Children's Hospital, Boston.

"What is best for almost all children, after the first few months of life, is to learn to fall asleep in a crib or bed alone in a room that is fairly dark and quiet," Dr. Ferber suggests. "They usually will be better off if they are not held, rocked or nursed and if they are not soothed with a bottle or pacifier, radio or TV."

Sounds like seventh heaven, but how do you do it?

"Put him down while he is still awake," advises Dr. Ferber. It's perfectly fine to rock your baby, sing lullabies or read stories. In fact, babies thrive on this kind of bedtime ritual, says Dr. Ferber, but put your child in the crib *before* he falls asleep. That way he learns how to fall asleep under conditions he can reestablish for himself after waking at night.

What if your child already has a sleep problem that is turning night into day, waking his siblings and making a zombie out of you?

If you consult your pediatrician, chances are you will get reassurance but not much help. "He'll grow out of it," "She's probably teething," "Let him cry," are the usual platitudes.

Dr. Ferber, a pediatrician who endured some sleepless nights with his own children, saw the need for more concrete help and made a study of the causes and cures of sleep problems in children.

In almost all cases he found that with a loving touch and a sensible strategy, most problems could be corrected in less than two weeks and frequently in less than one week.

Putting the Strategy to Work

Sound unbelievable? That's what Donna MacDonald thought. Her son Jeffrey would awaken and cry several times every night. Donna would pick him up, rock him or take him into her bed until he fell asleep, then put him back in his crib. When he was 16 months old, an utterly exhausted Donna sought help from Dr. Ferber. In ten days, Jeffrey was going to sleep without a whimper and hardly waking at all during the night.

"Dr. Ferber changed my behavior and gave me a strategy that worked," Donna explains. "I still enjoyed rocking him—but not to sleep. A little rocking, a bedtime story and a few hugs were part of the bedtime ritual. When I put him in his crib, I said 'Night-night, see you later,' and left the room.

"I let him cry for five minutes. Then I went into his room but did not pick him up. I talked to him lovingly, gave him a hug, then said 'Night-night, see you later.'

"This time I let him cry for ten minutes, then I repeated the scenario. If he was standing, I did not force him down. You do nothing that smacks of rejection. You are helping him learn a new technique. He needs love and support.

"Next time, the strategy calls for 15 minutes, then repeat."

Donna didn't have to repeat. Jeffrey was asleep before the 15-minute period was up. The whole scene took only 35 minutes. But sometimes, Dr. Ferber told us, the first session may take as long as two hours.

The second night, Jeffrey was asleep after five minutes of crying. The third night he went to sleep without a whimper.

There were several night wakenings over the ten-day period, which Donna handled the same way. Jeffrey began sleeping through the night, and Donna regained her old vitality.

A slightly different strategy worked for Linda Logan, whose baby was turning night into day. At 6:30 P.M., Matthew went to sleep without a whimper but with a bottle, and would wake at 2:00 A.M. ready to start the day.

To break him of the bedtime bottle, Dr. Ferber suggested offering one ounce less milk each night until there was only one ounce, and then no bottle.

To shift his sleep phase, Linda would put him to bed 15 minutes later each night. Bedtime crying was handled with the same 5/10/15-minute strategy used by Donna. In less than two weeks Matthew was sleeping from 8:00 P.M. to 8:00 A.M., and Linda no longer puts up with "jet lag."

Fear in the Night

Nightmares and sleep terrors—they both shatter the quiet of the night, but it is very important to note their differences.

When your child wakes from a nightmare, she is truly frightened and needs full reassurance and support. Stay with her. Hold her and let her know that you will keep her safe. This is more important than trying to convince her that there are no monsters in the closet. Even 13-year-olds appreciate this kind of reassurance when they wake from a scary nightmare.

After a nightmare, your child, if she is old enough, can describe a dream, but after a sleep terror there is no dream to report. A child having a sleep terror is not fully awake. She may cry out, scream, talk and moan all at the same time in a confused way. If you try to hold her, she will become more agitated and may push you away. When she awakes she will have no recollection of the episode, will actually relax and return to sleep rapidly. On the other hand, a child frightened by a nightmare will remain frightened and may be reluctant to go back to sleep alone.

At the time of a sleep terror, Dr. Ferber advises that you go into the child's room but avoid interacting with her unless she clearly recognizes you and asks for help. The child is unaware of your presence and may push you away and scream and thrash more if you try to hold her.

Sleep terrors usually occur one to four hours after falling asleep. Nightmares usually occur in the second half of the night when dreams are most intense.

After age six, sleep terrors tend to decrease. If they do not, or if they increase again, emotional factors may be relevant and should be investigated. Should your child's nightmares or sleep terrors at any age occur frequently, work with her during the day. Try to determine what is worrying her and help relieve her anxiety. If you are unable to resolve the stress she is feeling, then you should seek professional help.

The Right Attitude

No child, no matter how good his sleep habits, grows up without an occasional sleepless night, a frightening nightmare, a spate of crying in the middle of the night for no apparent reason. These are minor upsets that usually go away without treatment.

The most important advice sleep experts like Dr. Ferber have for parents, in order to keep minor problems from becoming major ones, is to help children develop a healthy attitude toward sleep.

The bedroom should be a pleasant haven, not an isolation chamber used as a form of punishment.

Don't expect your child to turn off his adrenaline like you turn off your car's ignition. Youngsters need a period of relaxation, a cooldown, before they can summon the sandman—a warm bath, a glass of milk, a story, a lullaby or just quiet talk about three good things that happened today and three good things you would like to happen tomorrow. This is a wonderful time for both parent and child.

Even with a bedtime ritual, every child has some nights when he will give you a hassle. Punishment, scolding and threats do not work.

Positive reinforcement frequently does—a star for every night the child goes to bed without a problem; ten stars earn a special treat, a coveted toy or a special privilege.

If your child stalls a great deal, you may be setting bedtime too early. Work out a schedule, then enforce it. Don't be wishy-washy. Consistency is the main thing, along with an appropriate bedtime ritual and supportive firmness. If you are lenient sometimes and firm at other times, your child will assume that this is one of the times when you are going to give in.

You have probably noticed that following Dr. Ferber's strategies means you will have to let your child do some crying. Some parents who come to the clinic express the fear that letting their child cry in a room alone might cause permanent psychological harm.

"Not so," says Dr. Ferber. The crying is much harder on you than on your child. Your child cannot understand what is best for him and cries when he fails to get what he wants. If what he wants is bad for him, you won't give it to him no matter how hard he cries, and you won't feel guilty or worried about psychological consequences. A poor sleep pattern is bad for your child, and it is up to you to correct it. Expect him to cry during the retraining stages and don't be overly concerned, Dr. Ferber advises, unless he does not get his share of love and attention during the day.

If you show your love and provide warmth and caring during the day, a little extra crying for a week or ten days will not hurt him at all.

Pet Therapy for Heart and Soul

It's exercise hour at the Tacoma Lutheran Home in the state of Washington, and P.T., an exotic yellow-crested bird called a cockatiel, is having the time of his life. He's sitting on the foot of 81-year-old Ben Ereth, riding in circles while Ben pedals vigorously on an exercise bicycle. The bird likes it so much that if Mr. Ereth stops too soon, he'll squawk at him.

A bizarre sort of activity to find in a nursing home? Not at Tacoma Lutheran. Three years ago, the nursing home adopted an angora rabbit. Then a puppy. Then tropical birds. The home's elderly residents have taken to these animals with a passion. And, says Virginia Davis, director of resident services, the animals have breathed enthusiasm into what otherwise might have been a listless nursing home atmosphere.

"The animals help in several ways," says Davis. "One of the cockatiels gives a wolf whistle whenever anyone passes its cage. That gives them an unexpected boost in morale. And the birds seem to alleviate the tension associated with exercise. They make exercise more acceptable and relaxing."

What's happening at Tacoma Lutheran is just one example of an increasingly popular phenomenon called pet therapy. Although humans have adopted pets for thousands of years, only recently have social scientists taken a close look at the nature of the relationship that people form with dogs, cats and other "companion animals."

At places like the Center for the Interaction of Animals and Society in Philadelphia and the Center for the Study of Human Animal Relationships and Environments (CENSHARE) in Minneapolis, they've discovered that there is something mutually therapeutic about these relationships. They say that pets relax us, help us communicate with each other, build our self-esteem and comfort us when we're feeling down.

In fact, many now believe that pets play a small but very significant role in determining how well, for example, a heart attack survivor recuperates, how a family handles domestic strife, whether a disturbed teenager grows up straight or even whether a nursing home resident like Mr. Ereth enjoys and sticks to his daily exercycle program.

Pet animals, in short, may affect our health.

The modern history of pet therapy began in the late 1950s and can be traced through three landmark events.

The first occurred in 1959, when the late Boris M. Levinson, Ph.D., a New York child psychiatrist, happened to have his pet dog, Jingles, with him when a patient paid an unexpected visit. Before anyone knew it, the dog ran up to the patient, a young boy, and licked his face. At that instant, the boy broke out of his usually impregnable withdrawal and started playing with the dog. Eventually the boy warmed up to Dr. Levinson, who went on to use pets as icebreakers in his practice and to publish a book, *Pet-Oriented Child Psychotherapy,* in 1969.

The next major event in the field was also serendipitous. In the mid-1970s at Ohio State University, psychologist Samuel A. Corson, Ph.D., kept a kennel for the dogs he was using for behavioral studies. Mental patients in the adjoining hospital heard the dogs barking and insisted on seeing them. Visits were arranged, and the trust and affection that developed between the patients and the dogs enabled some of the patients to trust their doctors.

Then, in 1980, the third and possibly the most influential discovery took place. While interviewing a group of heart attack survivors, University of Pennsylvania researchers Aaron Katcher, M.D., Erika Friedmann, Ph.D., and others unexpectedly found that people with pets lived longer after their attacks than those without pets. Soon after, they discovered a link between pet ownership and blood pressure.

The affection that people can share with pets is good for their emotional health, according to experts. The interaction between people and animals is calming and comforting, and it may even contribute to better physical health as well.

The lessons of these discoveries, according to those who made them, were that, in simplest terms, companion animals have two powerful assets—they help people communicate with each other and they help people relax.

Animal Magnetism at Work

Pet therapists have put these capacities to work in a variety of ways. Pet therapy is very often used, for example, to combat the isolation and loneliness so common in nursing homes. At the Tacoma Lutheran Home, Davis has found that the pets help many residents break their customary silence.

"Animals are a catalyst for conversation," she says. "Most people can remember a story from their past about a pet animal. And people are more comfortable talking to animals than they are to people. Sometimes a person who hasn't spoken for a long time, or one who has had a stroke and doesn't talk, will talk to an animal."

Animals also seem to draw everyone into the conversation. "Even in a nursing home, there are some people who are more attractive or responsive than others," says Phil Arkow, of the Humane Society of the Pike's Peak Region in Colorado, who drives a "Petmobile" to local nursing homes. "Human visitors try not to do it, but they inevitably focus on those who are most attractive. But animals don't make those distinctions. They focus on everyone equally."

A person doesn't have to live in a nursing home, however, in order to reap the benefits of a pet. Pets typically influence the communication that goes on between family members in a normal household. During a research project a few years ago, University of Maryland professor Ann Cain, Ph.D., discovered that pets help spouses and siblings express highly charged feelings.

"When family members want to say something to each other that they can't say directly," Dr. Cain says, "they might say it to the pet and let the other person overhear it. That also lets the listener off the hook, because he doesn't have to respond directly."

She also found that many people talk to and even confide in their pets. "I would ask people who they felt closest to in the family. Very often they said that it was the pet. One woman told me that her pet is like a psychiatrist she doesn't have to pay." Pets can even stop quarrels. "During family arguments, one woman used to say, 'Stop fighting, you're upsetting the dog.' "

Though it's still in the experimental stage, researchers are discovering that watching or petting friendly animals — not only dogs and cats but almost any pet — can produce the kind of deep relaxation usually associated with meditation, biofeedback and hypnosis. This kind of relaxing effect is so good that it can actually lower blood pressure.

At the University of Pennsylvania's Center for the Interaction of Animals and Society, for instance, Dr. Katcher and Dr. Friedmann monitored the blood pressure of healthy children while the children were sitting quietly or reading aloud, either with or without a dog in the room. Their blood pressure was always lower when the dog was in the room.

The researchers went on to discover, remarkably, that looking at fish could temporarily reduce the blood pressure of patients with hypertension. In one widely reported study, they found that the systolic and diastolic pressure of people with high blood pressure dipped into the normal range when they gazed at an aquarium full of colorful tropical fish, green plants and rocks for 20 minutes.

This calming power of pets has found at least a few noteworthy applications. In Chicago, one volunteer from the Anti-Cruelty Society took an animal to a hospital and arranged for a surgical patient to be greeted by it when he awoke from anesthesia. "It's a comforting way to come back to reality," says one volunteer. "For children, pets can make a hospital seem safer. It's a reminder of home."

Animals may also have the power to soften the aggressive tendencies of disturbed adolescents. At Winslow Therapeutic Riding Unlimited, Inc., in Warwick, New York, where horseback riding is used to help handicapped children of all kinds, problem teenagers seem to behave differently when they're put on a horse.

"These are kids who fight in school. Some of their fathers are alcoholics," says Mickey Pulis of the nonprofit facility. "But when they come here, they're different. When they groom and tack the horses, they learn about the gentle and caring side of life.

"The horse seems to act like an equalizer," she says. "It doesn't care what reading levels these kids are at. It accepts them as they are."

Ultimately, researchers like Dr. Friedmann believe that the companionship of pets can reduce a person's risk of dying from stress-related illnesses, such as heart disease.

"The leading causes of mortality and morbidity in the United States are stress-related or life-style related," she says. "Pets, by decreasing the level of arousal and moderating the stress response, can help slow the progression of those diseases or even prevent them."

Pets Are Comforting

But what is it about pets that makes them capable of all this? And why do millions of people go to the trouble and expense of keeping them? Pet therapists offer several answers.

For one thing, animals don't talk back to us. Researchers have discovered that a person's blood pressure goes up whenever he talks to another person. But we talk to animals in a different way, often touching them at the same time, which minimizes stress.

Another theory holds that pets remind us of our ancestral link with other animals. "By domesticating an animal, man demonstrates his kinship to nature," Dr. Levinson once wrote. "A human being has to remain in contact with all of nature throughout his lifetime if he is to maintain good mental health."

Dr. Corson, on the other hand, says that we love pets because they are perpetual infants. Human infants charm us, but they eventually grow up. Pets never do. They never stop being cuddly and dependent. Likewise, pets are faithful. "Pets can offer a relationship that is more constant than relationships with people," says Dr. Cain. "You can count on them."

Some argue that the most important ingredient in our relationships with animals is that we can touch them whenever we want to. "Having access to affectionate touch that is not related to sex is important," says Dr. Katcher. "If you want to touch another person, you can't always do it immediately. But with pets you can."

Most advocates of pet therapy are quick to admit that it has limitations. Dr. Friedmann points out that interaction with pets only reduces blood pressure temporarily and that it is not meant to replace exercise, diet therapy or medication. "Pets are just one component of care," agrees Dr. Corson. "They're never a substitute for other therapies."

Nor is pet therapy for everyone. "We want to protect the rights of people who don't want contact with animals," says Linda Hines, executive director of the Delta Society, a pet-therapy information clearinghouse in the Seattle area. "And we caution people against choosing inappropriate animals."

The safety of having animals in nursing homes is also being questioned. "We're looking at the incidence of allergies, infections and injuries associated with having pets in nursing homes," says R. K. Anderson, D.V.M., director of CENSHARE. "So far, pets appear to be one of the safest things you can do for a nursing-home population."

In other ways, however, the field of pet therapy seems to have very few limits at all. It is expanding rapidly. Chicago's Anti-Cruelty Society, for instance, which takes pets to 22 area hospitals, has a waiting list of 17 more. Meanwhile, at CENSHARE, Dr. Anderson and others are about to distribute a videotape that demonstrates how to initiate pet-therapy programs at a nursing home.

Then there's the research front. The Delta Society, for its part, has been awarding research grants to answer such questions as whether people's attitudes affect their response to animals and whether raising a pet makes people good at raising children. At the University of Pennsylvania, researchers are studying the expressions on people's faces when they greet animals. And in Washington, D.C., friends of pet therapy are trying to make sure that the government enforces a 1983 law mandating that the elderly residents of an estimated 900,000 federally funded housing units can't be barred from owning pets.

"There's a lot of ferment," says Linda Hines, of Delta Society. "It's amazing how many things are happening at once."

Have You Hugged a Hibiscus Today?

The first thing you see when visiting Jenny's is the plants. A potted Norwegian pine races the spindly avocado to the ceiling. Spider plants dangle a plush yellow-green web over the apartment's picture window.

You'll find Jenny here most days after work, watering, or carefully pruning the African violets on the end table, recharging herself after a stress-filled day as a medical social worker. Sometimes she just relaxes on the couch and gazes absentmindedly at her plants.

But whether diligent or daydreaming, chances are Jenny is forgetting about the patient whose file was lost in the computer and the disagreement she had with her boss. She is letting worries slip away and thinking about how her children like to hike in the woods behind the house, or about the vacation she is planning.

Jenny's plants, like the ones you grow out back or see on your way to work, are a fitting antidote for these high-tech, high-stress times. Potted on the windowsill, landscaped around the house or planted in a city park, trees, flowers and other vegetation can fascinate us, soften the environment and subtly remind us of life's natural rhythms.

Psychologist Rachel Kaplan, Ph.D., of Ann Arbor, Michigan, says that people "resonate to plants." Research by Dr. Kaplan, as well as by horticultural therapists, city planners and others, indicates that plants are excellent tools for helping people focus their lives and become more attuned to natural cycles and more aware of themselves.

Patrick Horsbrugh, an architect and city planner from Notre Dame, Indiana, calls it "phyto-psychotherapy," or "distracting" people —through cultivation of plants—from whatever their worries and illnesses may be. "There is something marvelous about looking at a plant every morning and seeing it grow," he says.

While many people get into gardening thinking they'll supplement their food supply, the intangible benefits gardening produces are, for many, more worthwhile, according to Dr. Kaplan.

Pruning Away Frustrations

It may feel as though the exercise you are getting as you plant and weed the garden or mow the lawn is breaking your back. But it is also therapeutic, breaking down any frustrations or tension you may be feeling, says Diane Relf, Ph.D., extension services specialist in home horticulture at Virginia Polytechnic Institute and State University, one of the founders of the National Council for Therapy and Rehabilitation through Horticulture.

"I remember as a kid I practiced 'horticultural therapy' on myself," says Dr. Relf. "I had a kid brother, and I would get so mad at him I'd go out into the yard and get the hedge pruners and prune the hedge. Now I've never told anybody what I pretended the hedge was, but by the time I got through pruning the hedge, I wasn't going to hurt my brother anymore. Working with plants, you can do something good, something positive, with the anger and hostility. You are turning it outside instead of turning it in on yourself."

Hard physiological data on horticulture's benefits (such as a slowed pulse rate) that would confirm this calming effect are just now beginning to appear, according to Richard Mattson, Ph.D., horticultural therapist at Kansas State University. "Of course," he says, "anytime you garden, there is a release of nervous tension and rechanneling of anxiety and factors related to stress. There should be some kind of calming process going on mentally, and physically as well."

Growing and tending plants—whether on your windowsill, in a garden or in a greenhouse—can have a mellowing effect on your attitude toward life and its daily stresses.

Lynn Doxon, of Kansas State University, recently studied pulse rate, blood pressure, skin temperature and other indicators in a group of mentally handicapped individuals in horticultural and more traditional rehabilitation workshops. She says that the final analyses show that the subjects were more relaxed in the greenhouse than in the other programs.

Meditating on Greenery

The mental pleasures we derive from plants seem to be based on the fascination that they engender, according to Stephen Kaplan, Ph.D., Dr. Rachel Kaplan's husband and, for more than a decade, her research partner at the University of Michigan.

If you have spent hours happily hypnotizing yourself while raking leaves or just minutes staring at the cluster of trees outside your office window, you know this fascination.

"The basic idea is that there are two kinds of attention," Dr. Stephen Kaplan says, "one that takes effort and one that doesn't. We tend to use the kind that takes effort much of the time," and this may be the cause of much mental fatigue.

"We are eager to rest that effort and attend to things that are inherently interesting, such as plants," he says.

Charles Lewis, horticulturist and administrator of the collections program at the Morton Arboretum in Lisle, Illinois, near Chicago, believes that plants' growth cycles reveal an innate intelligence, a larger force that is controlling them. "In our world, modern, man-made things just happen out of the blue. There is a lack of order. That's why it's nice to work with plants, because it is a situation where there is order, where things are nice and predictable."

Plants are also nonthreatening, according to Lewis. "They can't talk back, they can't bite you, but they *will* respond to what you do for them. A dog can get mad at you and growl, but a plant can't do that. It is totally benign. It doesn't care who you are or what you are. A plant is not interested in human values. You have to work with it according to *nature's* rules.

Roots That Bind

This makes gardens and other plantscapes great social levelers. "If you go to a community garden, you will find all classes of society working right next to each other, and they are getting to know each other," Lewis says. "In the garden it doesn't matter who you are if you grow the best tomato."

Beautification programs sponsored by housing authorities in cities such as Chicago and New York have prompted residents to take more control over their environment, planting in open and unused areas and policing the shared ground, according to Lewis, who first became interested in people's relationships to plants when he was asked to judge a New York Housing Authority contest in 1961.

Lewis was struck by the creative, nurturing effort put into the inner-city gardens. "As a judge, I would come back so full emotionally—I was just soaking it up. I realized that emotional gratification was an important part of these gardens," he says.

One particular plot, a Japanese garden created by the members of a street gang, made a big impression on him.

"They found out they could change their environment, physically change it, and not only so they would know it but so everybody who passed would know it," Lewis says.

Gardening is an example of an "active" nature experience, according to Dr. Rachel Kaplan. But getting dirty isn't necessary in order to enjoy plants; "observing" and "conceptual" experiences may prove as beneficial, she says.

Just viewing scenes of vegetation can "significantly improve" emotional states, according to studies at the University of Delaware. That work shows that people have a consistent preference for views including nature rather than those showing only man-made elements.

Getting Started with Plants

Of course, you don't need to turn your house into a botanical garden to begin enjoying plants. Taking a drive through the country or a walk through a local park can go a long way toward easing your mind.

But if you do want to start raising plants and you don't know the difference between potting soil and pots broken for drainage, the extension services of land grant colleges and universities are a great resource pool. Look for the service under the city or government section of your local phone book.

Ricardo Gomez, Ph.D., of the U.S. Department of Agriculture extension service, says that 45 states have Master Garden programs, which train volunteers with between 30 and 60 hours of horticultural studies in return for the same amount of time spent working for the extension service.

If you are planning interior plantscapes, you will need lots of light, according to Patrick Horsbrugh. "The bigger the windows, the better," he says. "Also, put pots outside in the summer and bring them in during the winter, so that you are constantly changing the position of the pots." He also recommends using trellises for vertical installations where space is tight.

Dr. Relf says professionals at arboretums, botanical gardens and nurseries can provide good information, but she recommends first talking to the people around you. "If there are neighbors who are growing plants and live on the same side of the apartment building that you do, find out what they are growing, because those are probably the plants that are going to do best at that side of the building.

"Look at the plants around you," she adds. "Find the ones that make you say, 'Hey, this is pretty, I like the shape of the leaves,' then consult books or specialists about what kind of plant it is and whether it is suitable to your location.

"Keep in mind that the specialist can tell you the ideal way to do things, but the ideal way might not suit your needs and personality. There is a correct way to prune grapevines. But if you happen to like your grapevine covering the woodshed, it is *your* grapevine. Do it the way you get the most satisfaction from it," she says.

In the most practical of terms, you should decide how much time you have to give to your plants and how much you want to spend on them.

"If you want social exchange and communication, join a plant society," Dr. Relf says. "You'll meet with other members to discuss and trade plants. On the other hand, if your need is to be creative or have control over a larger area, then maybe landscaping is best for you."

For those requiring immediate gratification for their efforts, Dr. Relf recommends building a terrarium. "Just buy a fish tank, ten little houseplants and a couple of rocks. You've got a total landscape that takes you three hours to do, and it looks wonderful."

Boost Your Brainpower

Water lilies double in area every 24 hours. At the beginning of the summer there is only one water lily on a lake. It takes 60 days for the lake to become covered with water lilies. On what day is the lake half covered?

How does your mind work when you read a brainteaser like this? Is it tickled pink—or tormented to tears? Is it too tired to tackle the task? Do you spend time puzzling over an answer or lose interest if it doesn't jump right out at you? Do you logically begin counting lily pads from day one? Or, without much apparent effort, does your mind leap to the solution? If the lake is totally covered on day 60, it must be half covered on . . . why, day 59, of course. Why didn't I think of that!

We all have days when our thinking is fuzzy and our logic defies reason, when we can't for the life of us remember some name or fact that was so familiar just the day before. On days like those you might want to trade in your gray matter for a new, improved model with rechargeable batteries and a software system that lets you discover the unknown secrets of the universe in one easy lesson.

Unfortunately, we have to make do with what Mother Nature has given us. Luckily, that's usually more than adequate. But it doesn't mean we can't make better use of the brainpower we do have. Here are some ways to do just that.

Poor Posture—Poor Thinking?

Ever feel like you just can't think straight? Check to see if your posture is putting a crimp on the blood supply to your brain, says E. Fritz Schmerl, M.D., teacher of gerontology at Chabot College, Hayward, California.

"The brain needs up to 30 times more blood than other organs," Dr. Schmerl says. "But allowing your upper body to sag—with rounded shoulders, head hung over and chin jutting outward—can create kinks in the spine that squeeze the two arteries passing through the spinal column to the brain, causing an inadequate blood supply." The result? "Fuzzy thinking and forgetfulness, especially as we age," says Dr. Schmerl.

Hunched-over posture can contribute to strokelike symptoms, known as transient ischemic attacks, which are brief blackout periods. Worse yet, disturbances in the blood flow of the pinched artery might cause a buildup of fatty deposits that can cause partial blockage, according to Dr. Schmerl.

"It's important to get a head start on proper alignment while you're young," Dr. Schmerl says. "Poor posture is a hard habit to break when you're older. Be consciously on guard to prevent this process of holding yourself straight, with your head back and your chin in," he says.

Iron-Poor Intellect

The brain needs a large amount of oxygen to function effectively, and the only way it can get it is through iron-packed red blood cells, says Don M. Tucker, Ph.D., associate professor of psychology at the University of Oregon at Eugene.

Some studies show that children with iron-deficiency anemia have short attention spans and trouble learning new material. They also show that boosting iron intake reverses these problems.

And Dr. Tucker's research shows that adults can suffer from related problems with alertness and memory when their iron levels are in the "low but normal" range.

In one study, for instance, the higher the blood iron levels, the greater the word fluency. (Volunteers were asked to come up with as many words as they could that begin with Q and end with L.) In another study, of adults over age 60, blood iron levels were one of the more important measures in determining whether or not the person had normal brain wave patterns.

"Getting enough oxygen to the brain is certainly part of its function, but we think iron also influences brain chemicals and pathways," Dr. Tucker says. "We know now that iron is heavily concentrated in a part of the reticular activating system. This area of the brain turns the brain on, so to speak. It maintains alertness. So we can't help but think that iron plays an important role in awareness and alertness."

Aerobic Aptitude

Exercise makes people feel good and can help lift depression. Now researchers are finding that it also builds mental "muscles" and may postpone aging's effect on the brain.

Researchers in Utah recently found that reaction time, short-term memory and the ability to reason all greatly improved in a group of out-of-shape people aged 55 to 70 who were put on four-month program of brisk walking. They were better able to remember sequences of numbers, for instance, or to use abstract thinking to correctly match numbers and symbols.

"I was surprised at the amount of improvement we saw," says Robert Dustman, Ph.D., of the Salt Lake City Veterans Administration Hospital. "We expected to see some results in some people, but we didn't think it would be across the board."

Aerobic exercise makes the body better at transporting oxygen to all its organs "so we are assuming that the brain benefits by receiving more oxygen," Dr. Dustman says. Those who showed the most improvement (their scores rose by 27 percent) had walked long and hard enough to be aerobically fit.

Stay Stimulated

Mental gymnastics may do as much as physical exercise to keep our brains healthy. In fact, there's evidence that the brain may actually increase in size when it's regularly "stretched" out.

Being in an environment that makes you use your brain helps keep your thinking sharp and efficient, says Marion C. Diamond, Ph.D., a professor in the University of California's Department of Physiology and Anatomy. Boredom, on the other hand, can cause restlessness, depression and a lack of fulfillment, all of which can interfere with thinking at your best.

Dr. Diamond has studied the effects of an enriched environment on the brain cells of young rats. After a month-long stay in a roomy cage that included playmates and plenty of gizmos to fiddle around with, rats' brains actually showed increased thickness in the outer layers of the cerebral cortex, a change that represents an increase in the dendrites. "The rats' brains became heavier and more chemically active,"

If you're feeling bored and restless, tackle something new — maybe something you've always wanted to do but never quite had the courage to try. Experts say that new challenges help keep the mind sharp.

Dr. Diamond says. The rats also went on to run a maze better than those that hadn't been in the enriched environment. "So they became better learners, too," she says. "I've seen the same results raising my children and teaching my students. The greater the exposure, the more adaptable they are to facing other problems."

Keeping yourself stimulated should be a lifetime pursuit, Dr. Diamond says. "Keep dreaming and satisfying those dreams. Keep looking forward, and each time you come to a lull, decide what new thing you want to do with your life, the new people you want to meet, how you're going to help people. Make changes, and make each change a new beginning."

Stock Up on Lecithin

Many of the foods touted as "brain foods"—fish, for instance, and liver and eggs—contain choline, a substance researchers are finding really can help preserve the brain's ability to reason, learn and remember.

For instance, researchers at Ohio State University recently found that mice fed a diet heavy in choline-rich lecithin or one of lecithin's "brain-active" ingredients, phosphatidylcholine, had much better memory retention than mice on regular diets. They took much longer to go into a back room in their cages where they had received a mild electric shock, meaning they hadn't forgotten their unpleasant experience.

What's more, their brain cells, examined under a microscope, showed fewer of the expected signs of aging, says Ronald Mervis, Ph.D., of Ohio State University's Brain Aging and Neuronal Plasticity Research Group.

"Normally, as the brain ages, its cell membranes become more rigid with fatty deposits and lose their ability to take in and release brain chemicals and to relay messages," Dr. Mervis says. This can cause memory loss and confused thinking. But a lecithin-rich diet seems to repress or delay this membrane hardening.

As part of the deterioration process, aging brain cells also tend to lose dendritic spines, the chemical receptor areas that are vitally important in passing along information. Having too few dendritic spines is like having a bad phone connection. Messages get distorted and lost. But older mice that were fed lecithin had the same number of dendritic spines as much younger mice.

"Despite the differences between mice and men, there are, nevertheless, remarkable similarities in the structure of their nerve cells," says Dr. Mervis. "I believe lecithin could help to repress or delay similar problems in man, although we have yet to verify that."

"B" Smart

The brain seems to have a special need for the B vitamins. Memory loss, disorientation, hallucinations, depression, lack of coordination and personality changes can occur with B-complex deficiencies.

Alcoholics, for instance, who sometimes develop thiamine (vitamin B_1) deficiencies, have problems with short-term memory. They may remember in detail that little café in Paris 20 years ago but not what they had for supper the previous night. Thiamine-deficient mice have trouble balancing on a tightrope, a skill that is normally a snap for them.

B_{12} deficiencies have been linked with poor memory and an inability to concentrate. And recently, researchers at the University of New Mexico School of Medicine in Albuquerque found that people age 60 or older with even a mild B_{12} deficiency had poor memories and abstract thinking skills. (They had trouble repeating a short story and matching symbols with numbers.) "I think it's likely that in older people, subclinical deficiencies can indeed lead to less-than-optimal mental performance," says James Goodwin, M.D., one of the study's researchers.

Thiamine is needed to produce and use one of the brain's major chemical messengers, acetylcholine, says Gary E. Gibson, Ph.D., a thiamine researcher at the Cornell-Burke Rehabilitation Hospital, White Plains, New York. And since the B-complex vitamins are chemically related and may perform some similar functions, it's possible that others are also involved in brain chemical actions, Dr. Gibson says.

Mind "Clutter"

How well your brain performs often hinges on your emotional state. Anxiety, with its turmoil of thoughts and rush of adrenaline, can enhance memory in some rare moments, but more often it dulls it. Physical tension all too often means mental confusion, as anyone who's ever botched a crucial job interview or important exam can tell you. A state of calm alertness, on the other hand, can help you think and learn at your best, says Stanford University psychiatry professor Jerome Yesavage, M.D.

Dr. Yesavage recently studied two groups of elderly people. Both were taught what's known as mnemonic technique to improve their ability to recall names and faces. (They associated a prominent feature of the face with a fanciful, visual image of the name. For instance, if the name were Yesavage and the person had a distinctive chin, the image might be of a savage grabbing the person's chin.)

But members of one group also learned a technique to relax their body before using the memory trick. They went on to recall 25 percent more faces and names than the group that wasn't taught to relax.

"Anxiety and worry actually clutter your thoughts and decrease your thinking ability," Dr. Yesavage says.

"We talk about processing capacity, which is the amount of information someone can be actively thinking about at any one time. The brain can handle only a certain amount of information at once, so if half its capacity is being used for anxiety and rumination, it can't be used for learning or remembering. It's being wasted. Getting rid of anxiety opens up more space in the brain to work on the task at hand."

Convincing someone *not* to worry isn't an easy task, but worry goes hand-in-hand with physical tension, Dr. Yesavage says. "Ease the physical tension and the mind follows." Calming music, deep breathing exercises, meditation, yoga, biofeedback and progressive relaxation training all help to soothe the body and free the mind.

Think You Can

Telling yourself you just weren't born smart, that you can never remember things or that you're too old to learn are good ways to sabotage your true intellectual potential, say David Lewis, Ph.D., and James Greene, authors of *Thinking Better.* Such negative thoughts "put your brain behind bars." They keep you from pursuing knowledge and learning better ways to remember. They can push you into a mental rut as you age.

Feeling good about your ability to learn is important to intellectual functioning, and it's one of the first things to be tackled at Mankind

Research Unlimited, a Silver Spring, Maryland, "superlearning" center that has turned high school dropouts into gifted learners and blind people into computer programmers.

"We tell people who don't think they can learn that they really have a lot more brain than they think and that they can learn to use more of it than they ever thought possible," says director Carl Schleicher, Ph.D.

His learning program uses a number of different techniques—listening to stately Baroque music, visualizing a quiet, private getaway place for thinking, and breathing deeply to create an aura of relaxed awareness. Then the student receives suggestions—that he *will* do better, that he *can* learn. He begins to picture himself doing that successfully, and his successes in real life are praised. He may also use creative imagery to bolster a sagging self-image. An insecure scientist might practice imagining himself in the role of a successful professional in his own field—Albert Einstein, let's say, or if he prefers a neater appearance, Robert Oppenheimer.

"Limits on learning are self-imposed," Dr. Schleicher says. Make the sky your limit by keeping your thinking powers fit.

A Consumers' Guide to Therapy and Therapists

Today, instead of lying on a couch or interpreting ink blots, someone in counseling is just as likely to be yanking the end of a towel held by a therapist and shouting "I want it!" That's the approach when the therapist is a proponent of bioenergetic therapy. The point of the yanking and shouting? It's a way of developing the capacity for emotional expression and increasing self-assertiveness and affirmative feelings, while releasing negative feelings.

Or if the therapist comes from the school of cognitive therapy, the client may find himself learning how to counter his automatic thoughts in order to build self-esteem. An example culled from *Feeling Good* by David Burns, M.D.: Instead of overgeneralizing and jumping to the wrong conclusion by thinking "Everyone knows how disorganized and selfish I am," a person would learn to think "I'm disorganized at times and I'm organized at times. Everybody doesn't think the same about me."

But why see a therapist? Isn't the best help self-help? Aren't *you* the best expert when it comes to controlling stress?

All that's true. But the therapist can improve and aid your own efforts to rid yourself of stress or emotional tension. He's someone to talk to—someone who won't judge, condemn, belittle you or bury you under an avalanche of advice, someone who will *really* listen. He's a professional; it's his *job* to understand troubling emotions and circumstances—where they come from, how they can warp your life and how to deal with them. In short, he's a life assistant, a guide for your personal growth, a friend.

Selecting the therapy or therapies that are right for you is a matter of learning the basic philosophy of each, determining if you feel comfortable with that philosophy, and then deciding whether your goals are compatible with what the therapy has to offer. Transactional analysis, for instance, may be helpful in improving your interpersonal relationships but may "bypass the inner person and deeper levels of feeling," according to Otto and Miriam Ehrenberg, Ph.D., authors of *The Psychotherapy Maze.*

What follows are descriptions of different types of professional psychologists and a list that provides the basics of some of the therapies that are used in stress management, adapted in part from the Ehrenbergs' book and from Marsha Linehan and Andre Ivanoff's "Guidelines for Getting Help with Problems in Living." Some involve a traditional therapist and client using a verbal approach. Others use the hands-on variety. Some, such as cognitive therapy, lend themselves to specific timetables. If that's the case, during the initial session the therapist may tell you how long the therapy is likely to last. In others, the therapy revolves around the relationship between client and therapist, and it's not always possible to predict how many sessions will be needed.

A Who's Who of Therapists

Your physician, clergyman or a trusted friend can be a source of referrals for a therapist. A word of caution before running to your friend's therapist: It's not always a good idea to see someone simply because that person helped your friend. "Your friend's problems may have been remarkably different from yours," says Theodore Wasserman, Ph.D., a New York clinical psychologist, "and the therapist's skills may not be appropriate to deal with your kind of problem." Since there are so many types of therapies available, first determine if your friend's therapist's approach is even suitable; maybe another method would be more appropriate to your problem and your personality.

You can hook up with a therapist by contacting a specific therapeutic organization or by getting in touch with the American Psychological Association, 1200 17th Street NW, Washington, DC 20036 (202) 955-7600 for the names of state psychological associations. Call or write the American Psychiatric Association, 1400 K Street NW, Washington, DC 20005 (202) 682-6000 for the names of psychiatric associations in your state or town. Your local community mental health association can also help you find therapists. Another source of referrals: a counseling center at a nearby college or university.

A first session with a therapist is considered a consultation. It's the time to find out whether his or her brand of therapy is likely to be useful to you. And it's the time to determine whether you feel comfortable and confident with the therapist. You will want to discuss your reasons for seeking therapy.

"The most important thing to ask them is the nature of their experience in dealing with your specific problem," says Eric Margenau, Ph.D., a New Jersey psychologist and author of *The Encyclopedic Handbook of Private Practice.* So if you're going to a therapist to stop smoking, for example, and he's a licensed hypnotist, that's fine. A psychoanalyst is probably not what you'd want.

It may matter to you how good a match you are with your therapist. While the job of a therapist is to be objective, be on the lookout for therapists who may have strong values that differ from yours. For instance, if your therapist is an ardent feminist and you aren't, you may have a poor philosophical match. Or if you're seeking therapy because you want to become more successful in business and your therapist is passionately antibusiness, you're not likely to get much sympathy.

Don't be shy when it comes to asking about any side effects of the particular brand of therapy. Relationships may change, comfortable habits may change, you may experience intense pain. Discuss these and other possibilities with your therapist.

Inquire about the therapist's training and qualifications. Therapists can come from all walks of life, and several of the therapies listed below can be done by mental health professionals of varying training. Don't by shy when it comes to inquiring about qualifications and background. First question: Does the therapist have a professional license from the state? Here are therapists listed by educational training.

Psychiatric social workers.   These therapists have a college degree and at least two years of graduate training in a program accredited by the Council on Social Work Education. For certification by the Academy of Certified Social Workers, a candidate must have a master's or doctoral degree from a program approved by the Council on Social Work Education, two years of postdegree social work experience and membership in the National Association of Social Workers. They must pass a written exam. Licensing procedures vary from state to state.

Psychologists.   These professionals usually have doctoral degrees (Ph.D., Ed.D., Psy.D.), although the requirement varies from state to state. The training programs may or may not be accredited by the American Psychological Association. Most state licensing boards require two years of supervised experience. It's possible after five years to earn a degree in a specialty certified by the American Board of Professional Psychology. Additionally, a psychologist may be listed with the National Register for Health Service Providers. Certified marriage and family therapists belong to the American Association of Marriage and Family Therapists (AAMFT).

Psychiatrists.   Psychiatrists must have a medical license. They are medical doctors who have completed four years of medical school and a one-year internship. Most psychiatrists also go through a three-year residency training program in psychiatry.

Nonprofessional therapists.   These therapists practice without training or accreditation. They may be individuals who believe their alternative therapies do not require formal education in psychotherapy and recognized credentials, or they may be opportunists. Says Dr. Margenau, "You wouldn't want to put yourself in the hands of a nonprofessional therapist if you have a significant problem. You'd only want to go to one if you want to work through something that's not too intense but that's bothering you."

Practical Questions to Ask

There are also some practical matters to consider when choosing a therapist.

Fees. Don't hesitate to ask what your therapist charges. (You should determine when you make your appointment whether he or she charges for the initial consultation session.) Many therapists charge on a sliding scale according to your income. Don't hesitate to ask a therapist if this is their practice. Some therapists make you pay for sessions you miss or cancel. Some therapists insist on being paid at the end of each session; others prefer to send out monthly bills.

Insurance. Check your policy to see if you have coverage. There is a broad range in what your policy (or your spouse's policy) may pay. Some policies pay for a good portion of your therapy costs, while others offer limited benefits. Some will reimburse for visits to psychiatrists or pay for therapy with a psychologist only if the patient was referred by a physician. Such restrictions are changing, however, as states pass "freedom of choice" legislation. And an increasing number of policies cover therapy by social workers.

Frequency. How many times a week will the therapist want to see you? How long will each session last? How long does the therapist expect treatment to last?

Some Newer Approaches

In the last decade or so, a variety of new therapies have blossomed. As a general rule, they offer practical and relatively quick assistance in handling stress.

Behavior therapy. This philosophy asserts that *all* behavior is a learned response to the environment. The goal is to change a person's behavior by replacing old responses with new ones. Most behavior therapists believe that the current environment is the most important in affecting the person's present behavior. Early life experiences, long-time mental conflicts or the individual's personality structure are considered to be of less importance than what is happening in the person's life in the present. The point of the therapy is to work on problems by working on a person's behavioral skills, not by assuming that there is one underlying psychological problem. A variety of procedures are used to improve the individual's self-control by expanding the person's skills, abilities and independence.

Among the behavior therapy procedures "stress inoculation" is the most comprehensive for treating the symptoms of stress. It teaches people how to change the thinking that is causing the stress, and it incorporates relaxation techniques and behavior planning.

Behavior therapist Theodore Wasserman, Ph.D., explains how this works. "Suppose Mary is getting a divorce. A behavior therapist might teach Mary how to behave in the situations that produced stress—how to relax in a meeting with her lawyer, for instance. The therapist would teach her to improve all the techniques that get broken down during stress.

"The therapist might have her engage in 'imaging.' If she had trouble concentrating in her lawyer's office, she would be instructed to image herself in the lawyer's office and behaving in a positive way, to see herself listening carefully. She would ask herself, 'What is stressing me? What am I saying to myself that's causing the stress? How can I think about it differently to reduce the stress? What can I do differently to reduce the stress?' She might be taught negotiating strategies: how to listen, how to respond.

"Also, the therapist would identify to Mary what she's saying to herself that's causing the stress. In cognitive restructuring she would be given other ways of viewing the events. Suppose the opposing lawyer is nasty. The therapist might say to Mary, 'He's only doing his job. He really doesn't mean what he's saying, he's just doing what's necessary to do his best job for his client.' The therapist would focus on the positive effects of the divorce, and what to do next."

Cognitive therapy.

This technique grew out of the work of Aaron Beck, M.D., a professor of psychiatry at the University of Pennsylvania. Its main principle is simple: What you think (your cognitions) may influence how you feel. If you want to change your feelings about something—yourself, for instance—you can change your thoughts first. Your feelings will follow. In one important study, cognitive therapy was suggested to be just as effective as a prescription antidepressant in treating severe depression. Cognitive therapists have discovered that when you feel depressed, most thoughts that create your perceptions of yourself and the whole world are grossly distorted. Cognitive therapy teaches that you can learn to recognize your distorted perceptions and change the way you think.

Gestalt therapy. The German word *Gestalt* means "meaningful whole." The goals of this therapy are to help the individual achieve a wholeness in which thinking, feeling and acting are integrated. Exercises in awareness help you focus on the "here and now." You concentrate on releasing or getting rid of old experiences that may be causing you emotional hangups. And body awareness exercises help you assess your feelings. You will learn what your facial expressions or posture might be saying about how you really feel. The awareness experiments and confrontational approach may enable you to experience feelings that were formerly blocked.

Hypnotherapy. "Hypnosis without understanding is a scalpel in the hands of a 12-year-old," says Murray Needleman, Ph.D., a Philadelphia psychotherapist who has a popular radio program. Like many other psychotherapists, Dr. Needleman points out that hypnosis itself, which is merely heightened concentration, will do little to help a person manage stress in the long run if it's not accompanied by high levels of faith, cooperation and trust. While the state of hypnosis can be therapeutic because it is associated with deep relaxation, many psychotherapy professionals caution that it should be part of a broader therapy strategy. "The importance is not the state but what the hypnotist should do with it," says William Fezler, Ph.D., coauthor of *Hypnosis and Behavior Modification: Imagery Conditioning.* He emphasizes the importance of finding a hypnotist who is also a psychotherapy professional. Many hypnotists have no training or expertise in psychotherapy and are unlikely to be able to help you by knowing what to do with the state of hypnosis once they've got it. Dr. Fezler warns that they can even produce the opposite of the desired effect. "A therapist using hypnosis has to know what's going on with the patients. Otherwise he could create anxiety instead of relaxation."

Primal therapy. Primal therapy gets a person to experience and express feelings that have been blocked. Techniques vary, but the more famous versions involve screaming out pain—the primal scream. What therapists try to achieve is an in-depth, unimpeded expression of your pain. In primal therapy you could find yourself beating a mattress to express anger. But it's not all screaming and beating. You talk with your therapist, too, although that's not the emphasis. One of the goals is to relive your painful memories. Once you do that, proponents of primal therapy say you will become a feeling person and "clear."

In its original format, primal therapy consisted of three weeks of intense therapy followed by months of group sessions. Now primal practitioners vary the schedule and format of the therapy. To learn more about primal therapy and to track down a list of primal therapists, write to the Los Angeles Information and Referral Center, 8380 Melrose Avenue, Los Angeles, CA 90069, or phone (213) 272-1478.

Rational-emotive therapy.   Developed by Albert Ellis, Ph.D., it teaches people to think rationally. By focusing on a client's belief system, a rational-emotive therapist teaches the client that it is the beliefs about events—not the events themselves—that cause an emotional upset, even though both may be disturbing. It's a short-term, problem-oriented therapy that does not dwell on the past. If a person were to visit a rational-emotive therapist for stress-induced problems, the therapist would first identify the stressors—a bad marriage, say, or job burnout. Then he or she would point out the effects these stressors have on the individual and his beliefs about them. Suppose the client believes it's wrong or cowardly to escape either the bad marriage or the impossible job. Then the object of therapy is to change those beliefs so that they are more in the person's best interest.

Transactional analysis.   This therapy was developed by Eric Berne, M.D., and popularized in his book *Games People Play.* It is based on the concept that people are motivated by social hungers in addition to biological drives and that the social hungers are satisfied by stroking—any act that recognizes another person. According to the theories of transactional analysis, each of us has three aspects of personality that determine our behavior: the parent, the child and the adult. Each of the roles fills a function for us, but if one role is either excluded or used *too* much, it can throw us out of balance and affect our relationships. Also, we can communicate satisfactorily only when our roles are complementary. Conflicts arise when, for instance, one person's "adult" is talking to another person's "child." Transactional analysis encourages you to get into adult-adult relationships.

What If You're Dissatisfied?

The Association for Advancement of Behavior Therapy's "Guidelines for Choosing a Behavior Therapist," by Marsha Linehan, R. Stuart, T. Risley, P. London, M. Parloff, J. Cautela and R. Bootzin, includes some sensible advice for those who may be dissatisfied with a therapist.

Talk with your therapist.   That's what he's there for. If you're angry or frustrated, if you're not getting anywhere, discuss your dissatisfaction with the therapist. "A good therapist will be open to hearing any complaints and discussing your dissatisfaction with you," say the guidelines.

Get a second opinion.   If your problems don't appear to be getting resolved, consider a consultation with another professional. Your current therapist can suggest someone for a consultation. If he objects to this, find a new therapist.

Consider changing therapists.   "Good therapists realize that they might not be appropriate for every person," say the guidelines. So don't buy the line that it's unacceptable to change therapists once therapy has begun.

According to the guidelines, "The most important thing you need to ask yourself when deciding to continue with a particular therapist is, 'Am I changing in the direction I want to change?' If you do not feel that you are improving and if, after discussing this with your therapist, it does not appear likely to you that you will improve with this therapist, you should consult another therapist."